INCENSE
TO
IDOLS

BY

SYLVIA ASHTON-WARNER

c. / cent

SIMON AND SCHUSTER
NEW YORK · 1960

TO YOU

I have heard of thee by the hearing of the
ear: but now mine eye seeth thee.

Job XLII: 5

ALONGSIDE THIS HALL I've not asked about I notice a mighty stone church; forbidding grey stone all the way from her foundations to the highest tip of her spire if not to the cross upon it; rearing above the low earthquake-fearing buildings about her, the only edifice with the faith to grow tall again. I notice the trees about her too, even gardens for some reason, and at her holy feet facing upon the main thoroughfare some picturesque stone seats to match. Would you call this a place to rest with the conflict of a church behind and the metropolis before? What a place to build a church at all for that matter . . . or did she get here first? Bang in the middle of an idolatrous city with the fumes of industry about her spire, shops, bars and traffic lights about her feet, jukeboxes contesting her bells and the boom of city all day. Are

3

God and Baal pals in these parts? But don't let me wander; where was I . . .

It is while I am resting on one of these stone seats this spring evening after hours of music in the hall nearby that I unexpectedly see you.

It must be you, mon cher.

For one thing you come out of this church and for another you are dressed as a minister. You come out from the back through some private holy door that people like me never darken. You emerge as casually as anything as though the black of the Cloth and the white clerical collar were the most common of clothes; as though life were the most usual affair.

It's not easy to see you at first what with the lights of the street and the shadows of the trees arguing for possession of you. But I can make out your head set forward, your shoulders broad and your arms and legs too long. Not handsome, not young and no doubt married. What makes the inner music I constantly hear lurch to a halt? There's nothing to my taste about you.

Now is the time to ask you for permission to practise in your hall that I've already been practising in and get it over and done with. There are you, here am I and beyond the church the hall. What am I wearing for this? The cream coat with the sputnik line and the blue stars at the throat. Will these aid the asking or are ministers immune to Style?

Now why don't I get up and do it? Why don't I stand up right here and now and introduce myself and ask for the use of the hall? I can't go on using a church hall without asking permission. But no, all I do is sit with the inner music profoundly silent. How unlikely from people like me. Aren't you men my natural habitat? Come on, Germaine, be yourself. Yet here I remain gazing up from one of your stone seats not unlike the drunk on the next as if ministers were immune to staring also. I hesitate . . . with the traffic drumming, the bells clanging, the jukebox wailing and the church spire surveying Mammon. Here I pause, though I never pause, while you stroll along the pavement towards me; your eyes brown, I notice, your brow low, your jaw sure and a look of serenity about you; all quite mere and usual. Here I wait on this seat set between God and Mammon undecided whether to get up or not until by the time you are abreast of me I am looking up at you so widely that you glance down in my eyes as you pass. "Anyway," you say to me, "bless you."

The way these evening bells plough their way through the layers and interweaving layers of sound in solitary stubborn routine; as though meeting the roar of the city head-on were a daily exercise to be tackled with patience and purpose. Clanging their industrious way through, round, over and under the drone of the traffic and its whine, bodgie squeals on the corner, urgent call of a rail car, endless beating of feet, a jukebox across the road, through the sober thoughts of the drunk on the next seat and my own inner music, an undersong to the din. The way they determinedly try to unite all these sounds on their chain of pealing chime. It makes me think of a man, sober and disciplined, ploughing his way through the diversities of humanity and trying to relate them all. These evening bells calling morality's shining message to the faithful . . . why should I think of you?

The next time I run into you is one night later in the week when I'm still practising in your hall; lingering, playing on in the darkness. The spring-afternoon sunlight shafting in has long since given way to the more passionate tones of a sunset. Absorbed in the argument and counter-argument of the concerto I've forgotten I've arrived in New Zealand and am working in a hall unasked for. Once again back in Paris I am such oceans and continents distant I don't hear the sound of steps so that the click of the switch is too sudden and the flash of the light too harsh. What a way to crash in on music!

5

What murder of a master! Are ministers also immune to sound?

Your broad outline in the doorway with your head set forward and your arms and legs too long . . . but I don't hesitate this time. I abandon the keyboard and rise con brio. I lower the top of the grand, pull the cover over, swing on my coat, walk across the stage and make my way out the side door and down the steps into the street and along the sidewalk to my car. I should have retreated last time.

But glancing back as I pull out into the traffic I find I have not quite evaded you. I see you standing out on the pavement, feet astride, hands pocketed, head forward and looking after me in a way that makes me sure you are thinking "Bless you."

"Cette voix qui perle et qui filtre
Dans mon fond le plus ténébreux,
Me remplit comme un vers nombreux
Et me réjouit comme un philtre."

P

EOPLE LIKE ME are just as likely as not to find themselves going to church on a spring evening, supported by a preliminary cocktail of course . . . actually entering this edifice of stone. It is hardly my natural habitat; it was the very last thing I had in mind when I began looking for a piano to use and it is the very last place where I will be likely to find playmates but who is going to stay home on a Sunday evening with a brand-new independence in a brand-new country and a studio in the heart of the orchards? Not me, mon cher, not me. There's a call for celebration and your church is the only place I can think of so far where I can go in a city without Sunday concerts and where I can say I know someone; you and the drunk on the seat. And clothes have got to be worn somewhere if only to church; I don't spend an inheritance on models for nothing. There is of course the risk

7

of running into morality but a good cocktail should take care of that.

Indeed and indeed I would never dream of going to such lengths, in or out of my senses, in or out of my cups, in or out of love, without seriously having to. It just so happens on this particular rainy spring evening after a whole day at the piano in my studio at Three Trees that I find myself absolutely having to. And with people like me it's do what you absolutely have to or face all sorts of discomfort and I can never help feeling how careless it is to risk discomfort if it's in any way possible to avoid it. So although avoiding it means church on a wet spring evening of all places I make it my business to get there however expensive the cocktail.

ANYWAY! . . . your "anyway" is catching . . . I paint my mouth with ballistic lipstick, perfume my hair, ease myself into the tubular suit with the radioactive line and into the shoes I brought out with me, jacqueline in perforated calf, string-bowed, take this necessary cocktail, back my car out to the road, streak along the highway through the surrounding acres of orchards with their promise of blossom to come, slow down into the city with its history of catastrophic earthquake, elbow along through the narrow main thoroughfare with its quake-fearing low buildings glistening with chromium, neon, traffic lights and rain, past the lofty Clock Tower I am coming to know, cross the railway line cutting the city in half, accelerate and break through the stone, iron, steel and concrete edifices dedicated to Almighty Baal and draw up at your great stone church in the centre dedicated to Almighty God, the only building with the faith or the foolishness to stand tall again.

And from here I walk through the rain, trees, garden, church bells, jukebox, past the drunk on the seat and the hymnbook man at the door, plough through the very-nicely-dressed, very-nicely-spoken, very-nicely-conformed congregation to a pew at the front beneath the pulpit, then plough on

8

through all the hymns, prayers, Scriptures, sermon, anthem, notices and the disputed and glamorous miracles . . . to burn incense to Clothes and to take another look at the minister.

It's no small effort.

Not that there is anything to fear as far as I know like the embarrassment of God in a church; not in this century anyway. For one thing look how full the pulpit is of Man, however pedestrian in your dull academic gown you appear to be from all available emergency standards. And for another where is he, as Raoul used to say, in or out of a pulpit who can transmit any spirit of God or of Baal without transmitting himself more. Raoul had never met him. Even the best of pianists, he said, leave something of themselves in the music. To the genuine sinner then there is little moral risk at all. As far as I can see one can use a church for anything without supernatural hazards; from celebrating a new country, wearing one's clothes, to taking a third look at a minister. Settling down in my pew directly beneath the pulpit I cheerfully do use your church. Sitting back in my radioactive line with uncovered hair, diamantéd gloves, Strontium perfume and an expensive breath I take this third look at you.

The thing I notice first again is the way your head is set forward on your shoulders with a short full neck. There is strength and belligerency in the setting of a head like this whether it is true of the man or not. You could be deliberate did you need to. On the other hand your manner is mild, which throws the first impression out of gear, so that I wonder if the belligerency is valid. As you open the service with a blessing I consider this contradiction and decide for the general mildness since it is more obvious and easier to comprehend for people like me. Yes, I conclude peaceably, you are a man of mildness and orthodoxy . . . I wouldn't go so far as to say "tranquillity," a thing of bigger implication; orthodox to the point of banality. Fancy making all this effort to come to

9

church for this closer look at you to find out a little thing like why I couldn't ask you for the use of a hall . . . wasting an expensive cocktail.

You've a poor brow though, I reflect as the congregation rises to sing . . . I don't stand I'm busy . . . square and low, which could do with a higher hairline. This dull look you men achieve when your hair begins too near your eyebrows repels people like me. But your eyes are good, I think, from this angle and in this light, and say a good deal for eyes. No romantic, quivering nostrils as musicians seem to go in for but your jaw makes up for a lot. Here's a jaw that would take no nonsense from people like me or from anyone else for that matter and is in accord with the forward-set head.

All told yours is a countenance I could hardly call attractive and there is much contradiction in it; is this the measure of you? Could you be self-divided and if so what about? But don't let me wander . . . I was on your face. It looks as though it had been blown by the winds of many a loud-mouthed market place; a plebeian face forgive the word; of a man of casual origin. A used lined face with the lives of others tramped all over it, with feet not overcareful. That's it: a face worn with the ways of the world. How old would I say you were now . . . would you be forty or over or under? Over I should say just over . . .

. . . The best way to avoid this sermon of yours I decide seeing the notes appear is to think of something else. Catch up on my own problems. A hard pew like a hard piano stool is just the thing for discipline; one can't smoke, can't drink and can't make love, not very well anyway. So as you consider your notes, survey your congregation and set off on your line of thought I cross my legs, survey myself and set off on my own line of thought. No less diligently than you do I examine my personal theme. You know what's wrong with my wardrobe? There's no master idea informing it . . . ooh how can I think with this running inner music! I brush my eyes to brush it away . . . too many differing styles and colours bought at compulsive random. Each a masterpiece of its kind but few of them related. This hand-embroidered Chinese gown now in rich dark-blue indigo, what has it got to say to the scarlet Russian jacket and the white dress with the gold leaves at the waist? There's more between the black-and-white lightning suit and the concert gown in white de-lustred satin. Wait for a storm for the lightning suit with its jagged darting stripes and until my music is ready again for the thrilling concert gown. Now where does the tamarack coat fit into all this and the contoured indigo wool and the cerise sheath and the white two-piece tweed? See what I mean? Disintegrated. Looked at in this way my whole wardrobe is inclined to be fragmented. Ooh and the white coat in the new luxury blend of rayon and acetate with the priceless look . . . no master idea informing them. No basic dominating colour, no one commanding style. A wardrobe should be inspired by one idea alone, even I can see that, like the composition of a concerto. Both clothes and music should, so Raoul used to say, take their character from the one personality. They should always . . . but something is disturbing my line of thought, what is it? I brush my eyes to brush away the inner music. A voice?

It is. It is your voice from the pulpit. Now didn't I pick quality in this voice of yours when you spoke to me in the street last week. As I was sitting on the stone seat one evening. I picked it from three short words: "Anyway," you said to me, "bless you." Now listen to what we've got. Ringing challenging thing it is, penetrating the most secluded alcoves of the mind. I'd go so far as to use the word radiant . . . "Hear the word of the Lord, we people of this city; we inhabitants of this modern Babylon! For the Lord hath a controversy with us. There is little faithfulness or kindness or knowledge of God in the land. Whoredom and wine hath taken away the heart, my people, and we have gone a-whoring from under our God!"

I sit up and uncross my legs and try to hear me this word of

11

the Lord. Don't tell me I'm going to be able to listen to a sermon if only to the voice delivering it. People like me who live by music recognise quality in sound. It doesn't matter in the slightest what you're saying. Listen to this voice of yours winging like a bird to the highest pillars, beating in exultation among the lofty rafters then grounding in marvellous diminuendo to the great Bible before you, filling the mind like a book with verses. Mysterious accident that led me a stranger to a stiff piano in a church hall, then to a stone seat in a street and finally to this voice! Astonishing consequence of coming to church . . . of doing what I absolutely had to!

What are you actually saying? I've already lost the place. You lift a page of your notes and lay it down aside and glance to the top of the next: "We burn incense to idols and we say to these works of our own hand 'Ye are our gods; in thee the fatherless find mercy,' and forget the Lord our God. We offer sacrifices to . . ."

Who else comes to this church? I might find some playmates here. For the first time I glance round the congregation huddled towards the back. Practically no congregation and from the look on their faces they attend to the meaning; whoredom, wine, idolatry and all rather than to the voice speaking it. No playmates here. Once more I listen to your voice injecting like an exhilarating love potion, to this minor paradise of sound, right through to the end of the sermon, through the following prayer, through the long last hymn and the benediction until with the hour at last over and with all heads bowed I hear the most bewitching sound of all; the beat of your step down the aisle to the door as the congregation sings Amen.

But when the hour is over and I rise at last with the others a new nervousness takes over. I've got to pass you at the door which is another thing altogether; quite another thing from being blessed in the street. If the Almighty Delusion is not in church then an almighty dilemma is. How can I give my hand to holiness with my perfume and lipstick crying aloud the city's idolatry and my line naming the idol I worship . . . the very things you've just been preaching? Silly thing I was to listen in the first place even to the little I did. Better to have heard nothing at all. At least my poise would have remained intact. Maybe I have erred in using your church and I don't see myself doing it again. This extraordinary consequence of doing what I absolutely had to in coming to church in the first place turns out to be a little too extraordinary for comfort; plainly there are pitfalls in church for people like me. I'll just thank you for the use of the hall and make a permanent exit. In the meantime however I notice I am not yet out and it is not as though I still have the support I arrived with; no cocktail will work for an hour.

No there's no way I see at the moment out of this crisis, of evading this latest consequence and sure enough at the door in my turn here is your extended hand. Everybody knows that a handclasp means good faith, even idolaters know it, yet where is my faith good or otherwise? How glad I am that my gloves are on! Very very glad that my gloves are on! So extraordinarily glad I have my gloves well on that when you follow me to my car shortly afterwards and offer me this same deliberate hand for the second deliberate time and I realise that outside the church good faith needn't matter not to people like me, I take one of these starry gloves right off for my bared fingers to receive it.

"ANYWAY," you say with a touch of belligerency, "how ARE you!"

I never answer this question.

"The music is going well?"

"No."

"I've heard you, oh I've heard you playing away in there."

"Have you?"

"You may use the piano and the hall any time and if anyone questions you . . . IF ANYONE QUESTIONS YOU! . . . tell them you're a friend of mine."

"Thank you sir I appreciate it." I withdraw my hand and

13

pull on my glove the diamantés softly gleaming. The rain has lifted and the trees are dripping and the pavement flashing wet. "I enjoyed your sermon," I lie, backing away to my car.

A pause while you see the lie, with no eyes for my clothes whatever. "Anyway," you say to me, "bless you."

" . . . Quand on m'aura jeté, vieux flacon désolé,

Décrépit, poudreux, sale, abject, visqueux, fêlé . . ."

I AM SITTING on one of your stone seats in the warm spring-morning sunshine with your mighty stone church towering behind me and across the street something even mightier; the massive concrete Town Hall. You know who's in that building? The maestro I have followed all the way from France. It's fifteen years since he left Paris but he's still talked about on the boulevards and in rue de la Colombe. So for that matter was I talked about when I set out to find him but what's new about being talked about? People like me can take it. For what's the good tell me of learning anything at all unless from the best master? Least of all the pianoforte. True his name is riddled with scandal but that's got nothing to do with technique. I was a child of course at the time of his trial and the ensuing uproar years ago but . . . neither have I even met this man yet but . . . and he doesn't even know

15

I've come but . . . but what else can you do when you have this "absolutely have to" feeling about learning from Monsieur Montigny? Life's too short to count consequences but the inner music breaks through and I listen.

. . . I wear the white one this morning. It is a two-piece dress in crease-resistant tweed with smart braid trimming. Lightweight and crisply textured for year-round fashion. Crimson lipstick against the blue of my eyes and my black hair is perfumed with Strontium. It's too nice sitting here in the sun, the inner music an undersong to the boom of the traffic; it makes the Town Hall opposite housing my compatriote in exile look gloomy and forbidding and out of character for people like me. But I haven't come from France to New Zealand for nothing and sure enough in time there returns to me this "absolutely have to" feeling directing all I do so that I find myself on my feet after all and crossing the pavement and now the street and here are the wide solemn steps . . . isn't it chilly in the foyer? and gloomy and echoing too. Chillier and dimmer still down the corridor to the right . . . there's his name mon Dieu! Monsieur Léon Montigny. Open the door Germaine and walk straight in . . . Never count consequences.

How dark the room after the sun! It's like youth running into middle age. What a big room too and a tall ceiling and all this austere panelling. Where is my compatriote in exile? It's very hard to see . . . ooh a German grand in the corner, ten foot! A table by the window covered in papers . . . Is that somebody sitting in the chair? How dark it is from the sun! A green suit and visionary eyes looking back at me over his shoulder . . . this look of not seeing what's near him. Deep places his eyes are in . . . deep shadowy places and lines wheeling round them . . . abject and pained surprise. So this is the man who sacrificed himself on the altar of l'amour and whose compositions always failed . . . so this is what exile is like; a feeling of dust on a life.

16

"It's hard to see after the sun Monsieur."

The portrait of a man looking over his shoulder . . . "Portrait of an Exile"—by Léon Montigny.

"I've just come to talk about the bridges of Paris Monsieur."

The eyes in the portrait move. They travel all the way from the top of my hair right down along all the places nice people don't talk about to my white feet and all the thorough painstaking way up again to my eyes. I fidget with a white glove.

"I suppose you are fearing Monsieur I am just another pupil come to beg the privilege of lessons. But," I lie, "I'm not. I'm no more than a compatriote in exile remembering the bridges of Paris. And the quays . . . le Pont des Arts . . . le Pont Royal and the bookstalls on the banks of the Seine and 'l'enivrante monotonie' of the evenings. I . . ."

"You may be that someone Madame, a Parisian remembering, but you are also someone else. If my eyes don't deceive me, if my memory doesn't either over the years, if you are in fact a physical reality rather than a . . . an hallucination, if I do actually and in truth see you standing before me, and if, when I reached out and touched you you did not dissolve into nothing . . . you are Germaine de Beauvais."

Mon Dieu!

He rises, not tall like you. "I saw you when you were a child giving your first recital. It was in the music room in the little house in rue de la Colombe. Over fifteen years ago but there are some eyes you don't forget; a dark-blue indigo." A pause . . . why this determined unconvincing formality about him . . . he looks at me the way men do. "I knew your father well." His fingers run in reminiscence through long curly hair. "Forgive me for not rising when you came in, Madame. Forgive such a lapse. And for not offering you wine. But the shock . . . the shock of seeing you walk in like that . . . it utterly confounded me. Too much to realise, to remember . . . to comprehend all at once. For me. I . . ." his voice drops to the minor, "I was never one for rising adequately to

17

an occasion, much less one like this . . . which is perhaps the source of my downfall. I failed to rise to an occasion fifteen years ago in Paris as you . . . as you probably already know. I've never," he walks to the grand and examines the keyboard, "I've never had the flair for assimilating situations and . . . and people rapidly. I can't take in at once too broad a canvas. I haven't yet assimilated exile . . . I haven't yet understood it or . . . or accepted it or . . . or found resignation. My responses, my reactions have ever been slow and I . . . and I remain surprised at the world and . . . and confused. To each day do I still wake a stranger." He returns from the keyboard to me and examines me as though he could not quite see. "I must beg Madame to allow me time to . . . to realise the breadth of this canvas she has . . . has evoked; the distant painful past colliding headlong upon the present; time to endure the . . . this explosive . . . recapitulation of the past. The chaos of it . . . the flash and the damage. All this it means to an exile . . . did I ask you to sit down? Have I? This dramatic appearance of a compatriote however young, however . . . exotic . . . your plunging from the sun into my shadows like this. Comprehension, my dear Madame, takes time."

He takes up a manuscript from the table and examines it as he did me as though to confirm its validity, then back to me again hastily. "Do sit down, Madame de Beauvais. This should have been said before." He takes my arm and settles me in the armchair nearby, remaining with his fingers still at my elbow. "Allow me," he says, "the honour." He remains hovering here in the way men do when they encounter my Strontium Ninety. "Yes I'm beginning to realise it and to . . . to believe it. At least enough to proceed with. Yes, do sit down, sit down that's what I mean. Have I said that? I perceive I have."

"Now," he continues, walking to a cupboard, opening it, forgetting his intention and closing it again, "no. I am not

18

fearing you are a pupil come to beg the privilege of lessons. I have your words right, have I not? 'To beg the privilege of lessons'? I've heard about your performance at the last concert of Raoul de Beauvais."

I look down and notice the clasp on my glove. I undo it and do it up again. It's a tiny gold clasp and works like magic and I continue undoing and doing it up. The sound of the click is soft and precise and anchors me a little to the present. "Madame," I hear him say formally, "accept my sincere sympathy and my deep regret in your loss of a devoted husband. It was indeed a great blow to us all. Even I have the right to offer sympathy; there are no frontiers in music."

"Thank you Monsieur Montigny, I appreciate it." Click, click. . . .

Silence once again but for the muffled drumming of the traffic and the deep-throated voice of a city at work and the close clicking of a clasp. I keep my face still lowered. A large shadowy austere room full up to its ceiling with silence with two silent people within it; two exiles if we must be maudlin. If I were a sigher, I'd sigh. . . .

As this silence unrolls itself, so does the past unroll; his as well as mine. Mine is born on flowing music like the Seine in the still of an evening; carrying beneath the surface of its waters the treasures and debris of a life in its twenties, now appearing and now disappearing like lost bodies as the river moves serenely between its ancient buildings and under repeating bridges fingering the quays and reflecting the people.

Pasts need silence to unroll so I stop clicking and listen. You never want to click clasps or chatter or make conversation and fill in gaps with forced words when this kind of silence comes or the past may refuse to unroll. And it's best for people like me to let pasts get their unrolling over and done with so you can roll them up again forever. Pasts sleep better after a good unrolling but only with a compatriote would I share this thing, countrymen are good at sharing. It's the way it's done

19

don't you think, mon cher? Most people's pasts are better unspoken with the mouth; let them talk themselves out in a common silence in the safety of the ever unsaid. Do you appreciate silence when the past unrolls, when the past unrolls unrolls? . . .

Wide-eyed upward listening to the music of the past . . . the sight focussed inward upon the opening movement of a life in its twenties borne on the river of music . . . until a sound halts it and I look down and brush it away from my eyes and I see him go to the same cupboard for the second time, this time knowing what for, and open it and take from it a decanter and glasses and bring them to the table putting papers aside to make room for them there. What care he takes in filling them! . . . a slow-handed meticulous performance. He passes me a glass in silence and takes up his own in silence and gazes at me no longer in incredulity but in the way men always do.

There is no clinking together of glasses, don't think that, while my husband's dead name is called in silence and neither of us drinks at once. He looks through the window at the blank wall there and I examine the wine he has given me. And here in its translucent redness I see with clarion clarity these pictures from the past he has summoned. I see again Raoul suddenly staggering from the rostrum and pitching dead among the first violins his baton in his hand. I see again the orchestra after a break in the music continuing to the end of the concerto while doctors climb from the auditorium and myself upright at the keyboard in white completing the solo for them; so that I prefer the present after all and look up at Monsieur instead, having had enough of the past unrolling.

He speaks gently and with care. "I was told you did miss a few bars."

"Only two bars and a half." I taste the wine then drink a good half of it. "Rhône Valley . . . magnificent! However did you get it past the import people? I'd like to get to know

20

some imaginative importers . . . perfumes and so on; cosmetics and . . . and fabrics." Another mouthful. "Tell me Monsieur," another red mouthful, "tell me, why does everyone dress the same in New Zealand? All the women in skirts and cardigans and all the men in grey? Is it a national uniform? Does the Government . . ." a knock on the door . . . "a pupil Monsieur?" I rise.

Sit down again ma chère compatriote. I'm no slave to Pig-Islanders. Finish your wine. All this has been so . . . so evocative and . . . and provocative Germaine . . ."

". . . and people are still talking about you on the boulevards and not just the trial part. Paris never . . ."

"You followed me this far . . . Germaine?"

"Not so very far."

"Ma chère . . ."

It's time to swing open the door myself and outside waits a girl wearing her hair too short and her breasts too long. I walk out in my "absolutely have to" way guaranteed to breed consequences. "Au revoir Monsieur."

How bright this New Zealand sun!

A KNOCK on my door.

A knock on my door on Saturday night? But of course. Doesn't what I want always come my way? True I know of no visitor this evening but anything could happen with people like me. It's no more than a matter of thinking positively and of believing that of course it will be.

I am drying my hair on the hearth rug by the fire and listening to the G Flat in mind, and thinking about techniques. I am in the glorious indigo of the Chinese gown, luxury-loomed and fashion-fresh, a spectacular garment amounting to a way of life, making every movement spectacularly beautiful but where was I . . . don't let me wander. Ooh yes Hong Kong slippers and all since I'm believing without any evidence whatever that someone will come. How unlikely to be alone on a Saturday night. I should be grieving shouldn't I? But people like me don't grieve. I should just accept it shouldn't I? But neither are we accepters. It's more comfortable to believe in the best I find and forget controversy with the Lord. As for what you said on Sunday about whoredom and wine taking away the heart, who wants a heart anyway. The whole thing's pleasanter without one.

"Anybody home?" The handle turns and around the door comes this wavy black hair, not cut short like yours. He gives it plenty of length to do its waving, letting it rear up from the forehead like a crowning glory so that it's the very first thing you look at.

"Ooh Doctor John!" I don't rise from the rug. "How very pleasant to see you!" Did I tell you about the romantic looks of this man? The dark Hollywood eyes and the black brows and deep features straight from a box-office film? Not that he's tall but everything's in the right place. Not too many bones like you, nothing angular or big-jointed, nothing so frankly clumsy. His head put on squarely where heads should be, and his neck more than just something to hold it on and his shoulders the correct tailored measurements. He's all you should be and are not. True, he's twice my age, his coat is the uniform grey of the country with none of the picturesque sweep of the drunk at church but he's Romance in Capital Letters . . . to look at.

"Boof! It's cold out there! Fire eh? Drying your hair?" Breezy, normal and that, at variance with the capital letters. Unromantic in spite of himself.

"Do sit down Doctor John. I've been short of a visitor tonight. Pull up that pink chair. You *must* be cold. Aren't these frosty nights merciless?"

"I can't stay. I'm on my way home. I had a call to the village. I thought I would pop in as I was passing to check up on the hands."

I do rise. "Of course you must stay a moment Doctor." I move towards him the gown touching the floor. "Give me that coat."

23

"Only a moment. My wife is expecting me. She was putting on the coffee as I left. And how are the hands?"

"Your shoe is wet."

"So it is. I went right through a plank over a drain; it couldn't hold me."

I laugh and kneel and begin undoing the shoelace my hair falling forward about me. "Give this shoe a quick dry."

"Have you a phone here? I'd like to ring my wife. I'm expecting a call up at hospital. No phone?"

"Not so far. This shoe won't be long. Dry the inside at least." I arrange it on the hearth and sitting in the chair he stretches out a leg and holds the wet foot to the warmth and groans in genuine weariness so that I go to the wine cupboard and bring wine and glasses to the table.

"All alone Mrs. aa . . . Jones? Y'know I can't bring myself to believe that your name is Jones."

"I can't bring myself to believe that yours is John."

"It's a shade more likely."

"If you don't believe mine I won't believe yours."

"You can check on mine soon enough."

I pass him a glass of Monsieur's wine. "Frost treatment," I say. "Wet feet treatment."

"Don't get that out for me. I'm still at work."

"Ooh don't be silly, Doctor!"

"No honestly. Not now."

"It won't hurt you."

"No . . . not me maybe. I've got another call coming yet." He lifts the other foot to the fire and glances at me reflectively. "No honestly I can't swallow the 'Mrs. Jones.'"

"Do doctors usually question patients' names? Check up on them?"

"We leave that to the coroner."

"Ooh don't bring coroners here!"

He still examines me in a furtive way. "Yes I expect you are short of a visitor. It takes time to make friends in a new country. Don't I know it. I've been through it myself overseas."

I settle down on the rug again and don't answer.

"You ought to join something Mrs. aa . . . no I can't say Jones."

"Could you say Germaine?"

"That's more like it. Germaine . . ."

No answer again.

"Yes you ought to join something. The B.M.S. or the Overseas Club or the French Club they've got one here. Or the Travel Club or the English-Speaking Union. They'd only be too glad to have you. You need to join something in a strange country in order to strike a root. Shall I mention it to Mrs. John? Eh? She's got a hand in things like that. You're too young and too . . . aa . . . too young to be sitting alone on a Saturday night, and she would thoroughly agree."

"But I'm not sitting alone on Saturday night."

"You will be in a minute. Well," he recalls his two feet, "a very nice fire and a very nice welcome." He rises reluctantly. "Now I must be on my way. Hands all right?"

I smile up at him and say nothing. He looks down upon me in the way men do, in the way men should, then up and round the studio, at the pianoforte, at the bed, at the flowers on the table then back again to me. Then he kneels and pulls on his shoe. "That's much better." He reaches for his coat and pulls it on. His long wavy black hair gives him a youngish look, and the clarity of his dark eyes . . . there's a boyishness in all his movements. Nothing romantic at all. He begins on the doing up of the buttons.

"Don't forget your scarf Doctor."

"Thanks. Well now! Would you like me to talk to Mrs. John about joining you up with something eh? Some club or other? There's plenty of life in Babylon."

"Do you call it Babylon too?"

"Everyone does after the Reverend Guymer. My wife goes to his church."

"Do you know the Reverend Guymer?"

"Most doctors know him."

"Do they?"

"You're always running into Brett Guymer at the hospital."

"Are you really?"

"We've come to look for Brett at our deathbeds; and at our lifebeds too. As a matter of fact I saw him a moment ago." He takes out a cigarette and taps it.

"What, is he in Three Trees right now?"

"He is with the little asthma chap."

"Oh . . . I see."

He strikes a match and lights up. "Well what about a club . . . Germaine?"

"I'm not club material Doctor."

"No? That makes interesting hearing."

"Think so?"

"Like everything else about you Germaine."

"Thank you Doctor John that's gallant."

"I mean it."

"Thank you so much again."

"You're quite at home with a compliment aren't you?" He moves towards the door. "D'you mind me saying that?"

"No."

"It all makes me think." He looks back from the door down at me. "I hope you don't mind my saying these things; it's pretty rough I know."

"I don't mind."

"I'm not one of these tight little Pig-Islanders you know. I've moved about. I know my globe. I did years of postgraduate overseas after the war. I know one girl from another, 'course you do in my job anyway. What I'm getting at is . . . I'll bet my bottom dollar your name's not Jones."

I comb my hair all over my face and look up through it back at him at which he comes back from the door. "Yes you've got me thinking. What are you smiling at?"

"I was just thinking of your foot going through that plank."

"I'll jump that damned creek next time."

"I can well imagine it."

"I'd like to have had time to hear you play."

"I'm not ready to play to anyone yet. You've got to fix my tendons first. Or fit me out with plastic ones."

"The next time this little asthma fella wants me. Well . . ." breeziness and briskness gone . . . "back to my wife and coffee. *And* the phone *and* hospital."

"Why who's so sick up there?"

"A little lady; a girl like you."

"What's the matter with her?"

"I'm hoping for the best but expecting the worst."

"Are doctors always in a hurry like you?"

"You might want me to be in a hurry to you some day."

"Not me never."

"You never never know."

"I'm quite certain I'll never be ill."

"Why?"

"Because I'm a positive thinker."

He laughs aloud like anything.

"You can laugh but I'll never be ill."

"We laid out a positive thinker last night at exactly twenty past nine. She was very religious indeed. Up to her very last breath she believed she would recover. So did the Reverend Guymer."

"I don't mean religious. You just don't believe in illness or pain. Or talk about it or think about it. And it's easy enough for me since the whole subject bores me."

"Why don't you think yourself out of your tendons?"

"That's no illness. That was too much practise after a long break, on a painfully stiff keyboard. Deliberate abuse of the tendons of the forearm."

"There's a lot in what you say of course." He sighs with a deep weariness. "I suppose about seventy per cent of my patients needn't be ill."

27

"I'm the living proof of it."

"But you cannot have had the experience to confirm it."

"Haven't I?"

"I may be wrong. Anyhow . . . this is not getting home."

"Thank you for calling Doctor John; it was very kind of you. Now I've had a visitor for Saturday night. I knew I would in the first place."

"Positive thinking plus." He smiles to himself and returns to the door and takes the handle. "Do you play a tango?"

I laugh then stop. "I could."

"You don't go in for that sort of thing? Jungle-rhythm stuff?"

I laugh again. "Ooh it's just a matter of getting hold of the music and of getting hold of someone who wants it."

"Right here's a bargain! I get hold of the music and you play it to me. Fair go?"

"What's 'fair go' mean?"

He laughs again like anything. "You'll learn soon enough." He turns the door handle. He's a masterpiece of contradiction. All this moonlight and romance in his face and not a shadow of it in himself. "Well goodnight."

"Thank you for coming Doctor John. My hands are worth another medical visit."

"And another time we'll have it out about your name."

"Not to mention your own."

"And you'll play me this tango?"

"Fair go," I smile.

Only his face is left. "Well . . . thanks for the fire and the . . . fire and the . . . welcome and the dry shoe."

"Come again Doctor."

"Cheerio."

"Bon soir."

The door closes and I hear his departing steps. I begin plaiting my hair reflectively. Furtive, New Zealanders about women, like some wicked secret. Why can't they glory in us like Frenchmen? Never mind . . . I won't be short of play-mates. Then I fall to listening to the G Flat again, Opus Ninety Number Three until I'm sick of inner music, sick of my secret infirmity that no doctor could cure, and get up and play it instead.

"Cette voix . . .
Elle endort les plus cruels maux
Et contient toutes les extases;
Pour dire les plus longues phrases,
Elle n'a pas besoin de mots."

I'M SLIGHTLY LATE for church tonight.

True I said I wouldn't come to church again but I notice I'm dressed at seven.

Yet for some reason it's so hard to set out for all my hours of dressing. Why can't I just pull on my gloves, pick up some collection and cruise off as I did the last time? They want us to go to church don't they? Idolaters in particular. Moreover this tamarack coat with the blue at the throat must be worn somewhere, a slim wrap-skirted sheath in Talbot's blend of eighty per cent wool and twenty per cent rabbit hair and the maestro rose to the level of poetry over the contour belting and look at my favorite footing, the wisp-weight wedge, a tweed-loving leather slenderly poised but don't let me wander and lose the place . . . anyway masterpieces like these from the hand of man were hardly created for seclusion. Yet here is this matter of morality again rearing its chilly head and this crisis of a hand at the door. It amounts to a discomfort this going to church but it's also a discomfort not to. Is either of these worth it? Ooh for an orchestral concert.

I mix myself a cocktail, one well known on the Left Bank called the Rocket guaranteed to send into orbit. Given time and the correct ingredients the chilliest morality warms. After a drink and a little more thought this chilly morality does warm. The discomfort of going probably is worth it. There are after all, argues the Rocket, compensations in that church: for one thing you can at least listen to the voice itself . . . more than listen to be frank . . . whether or not its glory has any relation to its meaning and whether you register what is said or not. And for another even should you accidentally run into a little meaning it is at least on an adult level whether you agree with it or not; all of which, continues the Rocket, is no mean consideration to people like me. Indeed and indeed as the ingredients finger their way down into the secret subversive places igniting every fuse I've got the whole prospect of going to church, while hardly rising to the level of irresistibility, at least seems a good idea. Abstinence could never do this.

The Citroën springs forward as it stops with a jerk in true Continental fashion. The service has already begun.

Yet here are several advantages. Walking through the shadows of the trees I am received by the drunk on the steps. What a picturesque tableau he makes draped against the portal. Tall had he been upright, his overcoat hanging open from the shoulders with a sweep that would have enthralled Monsieur, his lowered hat hiding his upper features and whiskers hiding the lower. Reflectively he watches me mount the steps then speaks it seems to himself. "Outrageous beauty," he remarks.

"Who me?"

"Oh you do speak? You are real then? I wondered." His shoulders are old but his voice is not. He sways a trifle from the portal and carefully recovers it. His breath is considerably more expensive than mine. "I've been wondering whether or not you are real."

"Have you really?"

"Yes."

"How interesting."

"Yes I'm afraid so. I'm always being interesting. I know it's unfortunate but I'm unable to help it. I expend a large part of my meagre energies trying not to be interesting but I fail again and again."

I smile and he continues, "She had a touch of dark blue at her throat indigo blue, an overflow from the blue of her eyes."

"Thank you but it's all deliberate of course, the blues matching I mean." The lips within the beard make me sure he's young.

"Do you mind if I reach forward and touch that face? I can't bring myself to believe it." He does in fact lift a hand trembling so extravagantly that I laugh again in this city.

"She laughed gaily," he continues, "displaying a row of very clean teeth with a flash of gold upon them."

"That gold grew there." I laugh like anything at my own joke I can be very funny. From within the forbidding church the first hymn is under way something about forgiving our foolish ways, the surge of it solemn and holy. Beneath it I hear him speak theatrically, " 'Her face is like a petal on a wet dark bough.' "

"So would yours be if you spent what I do on it."

He examines me closely not in the way men do. "Forgive me if I'm serious a moment. I know it's a risk. I'm at my most irresistible when serious. But I wish to discover something. Money can't buy eyes that colour neither do women grow them. Are you quite sure they're real or are you making it up? Or has some irresponsible artist painted them on you without checking his pigments? Indigo eyes would never be accepted by the most advance-guard gallery, not from the most respected surrealist. A man . . ." The inner music, the beat in the bass with the cellos, beat, beat . . . beat . . . I brush my eyes to brush it away. "I beg your pardon? What were you saying?"

"I was saying a man would forget the wife of his bed before he forgot that mouth. 'Sulky lips shaped for sin . . .' "

"Don't be silly."

"Don't be silly? But I *try* to be silly. I'm a professional fool. One needs to be very clever to be as silly as me." He pauses and regroups. "The shape of her face would shame a heart . . . a heart is no more than a copy. Her hair furls up from the temples to continue the line of the ventricles, dipping in the centre of the top. Hair like night deepening and swelling at the nape of the neck. It looks like a headdress for *Swan Lake*."

"It has taken me since morning to do it. Glamour takes time you know."

"It also takes hair I believe."

"If you'd seen it yesterday when I was practising you'd use another language. Or when I wake in the morning. Haven't you ever seen behind the scenes of glamour?"

"I'm determined to have you glamorous and mysterious. I'm short of glamour and mystery."

"But I'm the most ordinary mortal. It's so much easier to be ordinary." I step on up into the porch but he touches my arm.

"I say what did you think of my homage though? Don't you think it was . . . aa . . . highly inventive?"

I laugh again before entering solemnity. "It's the best so far in New Zealand."

He collapses with every care upon the step. "I must let you get on with your aa . . . devotions. The Reverend Guymer will be missing you." He looks up from the step. "What are

33

you listening to all the time? You look as though you're hearing something."

I pause irresolute then the Rocket speaks. "That is my secret infirmity." Now I walk on in and leave him.

Opening the door I find a second advantage in being late. Once more I am received but this time by a hymnbook. It comes from a man with the easiest smile I have ever seen and a clear decade older than me. He's dark isn't he or is he fair? I can't really tell. He's dressed in something I don't notice and by the hunger in his hand he's married. He stands upright without draping anything like the drunk, his breath has no distinction and he's not concerned about being interesting. Unlike Monsieur's his hair is both cut and combed and he wears grey rather than green. He does not look all moonlight and romance like Doctor John and his legs and arms and joints are not all too long and out of place like yours. All of which as the congregation makes the last verse and as he puts this hymnbook in my hand, the hand he is not still holding in the way men do, his eyes shamelessly taking leave of him . . . where was I now? this is an involved sentence . . . ooh yes all of which I take careful note of. Good! I got it finished.

And now here is the final advantage. Gliding up the aisle through the singing worshippers to my pew beneath the pulpit I can prove the potential of this coat. Not too quickly now and keep in step with the hymn, four crotchets to the bar. I'm not saying this doesn't take courage; there's some fine distinction between a church and a concert chamber that I can't quite put my finger on but what if I am a little nervous? No one can stop once in orbit.

I see no reason to stand up and sing these hymns do you? The Christians will see to that. Would you stand up and sing miles and miles of hymns if you had already put in seven hours a day during the week at music? Besides all this standing

34

and sitting and such you never do at a Sunday Concert and it's hardly a reward for the hours I have already spent on my feet dressing for church in the first place. Such a fearful lot of verses there are with seven or eight lines in each all about a soul I haven't got. Also if I did open the hymnbook there is the risk of finding that the words sometimes have meaning which might take my mind off what I came here for originally, assuming I knew that myself. Moreover if I do listen to the tune there are so many verses that I would run the risk of coming to know the damn thing in the end so that it might take the place of the inner music and who wants to be listening to inner hymns for the next few days. What would Almighty Baal think about that? I'd be excommunicated for a heretic. Deny the outer ear Germaine for the inner and keep the music you know . . .

When the time comes however for the reading of the Scriptures I'm all outer ear. The chords of your voice are something I can take with or without relevant meaning. I lay one hand upon the other, look up at you above me and surrender myself all too carelessly to this sound "qui parseme des étoiles mon coeur. . . ."

You ponder a moment on the outsized Bible before you. Is it possible that otherwise responsible citizens still read from this book written so many centuries ago, with twentieth-century fiction what it is? How can these ancient thought forms and terminology compare with our atomic-age best sellers? How can sane modern people endure it? Why do you persist in teaching so outdated a message with science and philosophy what they are? How can a graduand like you still turn for wisdom to this lifeless relic of the past? Isn't morality irrelevant enough in this age of nuclear fission without its also being remote? Morality is no longer a success in this century so how can it possibly be popular? Success is valued by people like me and we judge everything and everybody by it. And there are millions and millions of people like me. Yet here you are one of this extraordinarily stubborn minority still preaching morality; still putting a premium on it; amazing abnormality! Fascinated I watch you examine the page before you; a man, I note, now that I have met you and have seen you in action, not without a certain serenity . . . although I still balk on the word "tranquillity."

"Hear the Word of the Lord as it is contained in the book of Hosea!" you charge with something of that latent belligerency I noted in your conversation last Sunday. You lift your eyes to see if we are attending. You don't find us at once however. We're not in the front pews, nor yet in the middle but huddled towards the back. As for me I might as well not be here. Don't ministers look directly beneath their pulpits? My Strontium Ninety perfume cannot be stront enough, not enough fall-out apparently or rise-up to be more accurate. To be seen I should sit at the back. It takes a while to pick up your ways. However you seem to be satisfied that some are attending enough to go on with anyway and once more you turn to the Bible: " 'And the Lord said unto Hosea, "Go, take unto thee a wife". . . So he went and took Gomer . . .' " And here we have the old story of an unfaithful wife whose husband took back from her the vineyards he had given her in love. . . .

You lift your eyes from the page and dwell on a large bowl of spring flowers nearby, speaking to them rather than to us, weighing your words with emphasis. "May God add His blessing to this reading to us of His word and to His name be glory and praise."

After this story I try to listen to your sermon but one glance at the notes you bring out that we've all got to plough through, and I change my mind and settle for the voice alone. And in no time it has caught me up again like a whirlwind or a tornado as they call it out here. What a relief to have the inner music silenced! For once I am able to listen wholly and utterly to a sound other than music and if ever sensibility spoke to me through a voice it speaks to me through yours proclaiming God's passion for his a-whoring people and the profundity of his forgiveness whether I wish it to or not. Plainly you set off to church on an intoxicating drink also with ingredients more potent than mine; some pure and divine liquor like clear fiery wine, for your "mystic deliria" would spark religious fervour from a graven image itself. "Fierce updraughts of the spirit force you to the stars" so that I all but leave the ground myself. Can morality be so chilly? Are there garments more thrilling than clothes? Is it conceivable that your Almighty Delusion may not be all delusion? By the time the sermon is over, by the time your voice has abated and your hands have come to rest I find myself taking a second thought about you and a third one about myself.

So that I leave the church during the last hymn. To meet this hand of yours at the door tonight may not be worth the risk; it may promote a new colour, a new shade rather, in my values which has nothing to do with Style . . . nothing to do with things like the satin, hand-embroidered slippers obtained only intricately through Hong Kong . . .

So that when I once more drive off up Heretaunga Street as far as the Clock Tower and park there and listen to the sounds of a city while Christians take themselves off home to supper I wait there a long long time before I wheel and return to the Town Hall opposite and look for the light beneath my compatriote's door. And it is not until a couple of hours after something rational in C Major at his keyboard that I can bring myself down to earth. Indeed into the prostration of dawn at Three Trees I am still seeing your face during the sermon like some futuristic painting with contours of shadow and light, your broad shoulders at times crouched, your hands embracing and releasing each other and your voice winging and grounding through the lofty church as you preached God's wrath and forgiveness. It is not until morning comes and Léon lies sleeping that I shed the eye of fever and can see with the ribald stare of the city. On my own inconsequent level once more and with my rationalism intact I recover my peace of mind . . . I reclaim from you my vineyards.

I must keep my head another time in church and avoid the pitfalls thereof. I must keep my head anyway for that matter and avoid the church altogether.

I HAD NO TROUBLE picking up this Steinway even though the man still wanted it.

He argued that he didn't see how he could replace it with the import restrictions what they are. However he gave it up never mind how.

It's only a six-foot but in good body and voice having been bought from the City Council by a band leader blessed with an early training in classics not to mention an early training in marriage, who saw no reason to lock it for twenty years or anything else for that matter. So that it has been understood as well as used. I like a well-used instrument don't you? I like flexibility in the keys and action, the pedals not too stiff to be workable. Playing this Steinway is nothing like the work playing the Brinsmead in the hall which had been locked up by a bachelor. The thing is to let someone else do the breaking in of a piano or a man then you come in on the trained animal; far easier to play either of them with the mechanism loosened up. Don't you think? Not that Steinway has anything like the power and tone the Brinsmead had conserved during its twenty years' continence. Steinway is all too well loosened up having little left over to say. Maybe whoredom and wine hath taken away the heart like the other inhabitants of Babylon who according to you a-whore from under their God . . . playful defection. Notice me quoting the Bible? But don't let me wander, where was I? . . . ooh yes give me the flexibility of this instrument any day for solid routine practise. After all it only cost me £450 or was it £540? Anyway! to quote you, it'll have to do till the imports let up like a few other things I'm short of.

After all I've had your permission to use that pent-up bachelor in the hall any time whenever I feel equal to the effort or need the real thing, for all it's so hard to play. Don't forget it has cost me a tendon in the left forearm over which I'm getting to know Doctor John much better. But ooh it's no good dreaming back to the ten-foot in the rue de la Colombe. Even people like me can't have everything which may or may not be a good thing.

Steinway looks reasonably at home against the wall on the sunny side, the north they call it out here. Everything geographical and geophysical in New Zealand they've got all backwards. The sunny side is the north and the cold side the south; the Far East is the Near Northwest . . . work that out. Spring is in winter and winter is in spring and don't mention language or currency . . . the New Zealand pound mon Dieu! and have I had enough of their tea! Anyway! . . . I say aren't capital letters catching? . . . where was I? Ye-es Steinway looks reasonably well enough at home or at least as at home as I am, as at home as anyone could be who was not "Made in New Zealand."

The main thing about this studio, this cottage with the inside walls carved out, that can never be boring is that there's not another habitation within range of the sound of a piano. No worrying about people next door when you're practising, no near neighbours to check on what time your visitors arrive or leave to spread it all round the village or to examine my lingerie on the line in new luxury blends of rayon and acetate, drip-dry, wrinkle-free, deceptive, some of the best craftsmanship in the world, the "world" meaning Paris. . . . a great deal of time is given to crafting these little gems of accuracy at five hundred dollars apiece . . . where is the place again now? . . . yes and the orchards surrounding for privacy, the trees bare-limbed so far with no more than swellings where the blossoms will be, all of which . . . all of which . . . the music floods forward from the back of my mind and I've lost the place after all . . .

. . . Look at these trees round the studio, interesting beings they are with voices that are seldom stilled. Tender voices they have that neither clash nor clang nor hack nor attack. I haven't found them yet without something or other to say however faint the wind. Talking away to each other like intimates which by now no doubt they are. Leaning to one side they tell a story to this one then swaying over to the other they repeat the whole thing. Three of them are very big, the tallest the carpenters said was a gum. Mostly boughs it is whitish and round like arms imploring endlessly for something in the sky as you were last Sunday. Silly things the two of you are wasting time and life wanting the ever invisible. Better the stolid dark tree beside him, rough and reasonable, his trunk firmly in the ground and wanting only what he can see for himself and considerably the healthier for it, the shadow he casts a foolproof argument with no sunlight patching through. A totara they told me proudly, a native they added profoundly. Better also than the beauty at the front of the studio whose name nobody knew, throwing back the sun from her

41

bright foliage in a crown of diamantés, believing only in herself.

The grounds themselves cannot have been attended to in lifetimes, long, thoroughly-lived-in lifetimes. There may have been gardens once by the colour pockets of long-forgotten flowers but there's no clue now to where. There'll need to be a drive carved from the garage to the gate though, there's a limit to the gymnastics of a low-bodied Citroën. Besides I'm one of those people who like to be able to get in or out of a garage or a situation with ease whether it is a consequence of my own doing or not. And there really should be a fence. What is the function of a gate however primly closed with any amount of access from either side? Anything and anyone from pigs to reporters could stray in here if they wished. I pause, standing in the long grass in the Saturday morning sun and listen to the music within. . . .

. . . It's cold inside after the sun outside and I put on the fire another of the timber ends the carpenters have left lying everywhere and set the sponge-rubber cushion on the piano stool. Now I tie my hair behind my back to keep my back warm and pull on the black velvet smock . . . where are those frightful old slippers I keep for this job? . . . and I settle down at the keyboard. If the men who look at me in the way men do could only see me now. . . . Now I roll up my sleeves, undo my brassière and get down to business.

"Cette voix . . .
Non, il n'est pas d'archet qui morde
Sur mon coeur, parfait instrument,
Et fasse plus royalement
Chanter sa plus vibrante corde,
Que ta voix . . ."

I CAN'T GET my thinking done as well during the sermon
these days, the minister interrupts me.

It's a loss.

There are still the hymns to think through but how can I
be in time even for these? So far one Rocket would get me to
this church like other reasonable beings but those times appear to be over. Ever since I found myself using your church
for other than dress I have found myself other than assured
which is hardly in the interests of Style. My inclination to
hear your voice is equalled only by my reluctance to hear it.
Didn't I say there might be pitfalls in church for the unwary?
This voice of yours in its vigour and intimacy addresses every
organ I've got. How could I have foreseen such a consequence
when I first came to church one evening? I just don't know
what's happened to my poise so indispensable to Style. A

bottle accompanies me in the car now, a glass too and here I am holding a one-girl cocktail party outside the church to help propel me in. Making two. And I need to give them time to work so that by the time I have gone into orbit, greeted the drunk on the steps, opened the door, lifted my two eyes to the hymnbook man, zoomed up the aisle and knelt a moment for the look of it, there's little more than the sermon left.

All so unfavourable to thinking.

It's no small misfortune to people like me that you should preach with this voice. Everyone knows that a sermon is delivered to be thought, day-dreamt or slept through but it's impossible when you are speaking. Moreover since even I cannot always avoid registering a sentence or two, on occasion a paragraph or two, I find foreign thoughts intruding of a singularly distasteful variety. Instead of thinking about the principles of Style I am thinking about those of living, whereas people like me who have put so much industry into the finer nuances of idolatry can't stand this kind of principle. It's a little embarrassing to say the least and to people like me irrelevant. Loving one's fellow *man,* for instance, sincerity in relationships, the brotherly covenant, the way of the meek, reverence for God and obedience to his holy will and so on. What about loving one's fellow man, an accomplishment of mine, fun in relationships, the lover's covenant, the way of the inconsequent, reverence for Style and Baal's holy will? Surely we sinners hold some ground but with sermons like yours we'll lose it. Indeed the time may come when with the spirit in glory and the flesh in shame I may no longer see fit to use this church at all; in or out of orbit.

Do you think holiness is for people like me? This uncomfortable rendering? One of these innocent spring evenings from the sheer weight of suggestion I'm going to find myself *wanting* to hear. I might find myself hearkening unto irrelevancies like the consequences of Rockets and the size of the country's drinking bill; to the discourtesy of being late, the subversiveness of Strontium and that compatriotes are not a good idea. Before long who knows I may be reminded of St. Paul's aversion to a woman's bare head, reprieved for the radioactive line, funproof lipstick and for my blue listening eyes. Who knows I might find myself *taught something*. And you never want to try teaching people like me because people like me can't stand it.

Does my presence not contribute to holiness I wonder? To the atmosphere of the lilies, the anthem and prayer? "Ne suis-je pas un faux accord dans la divine symphonie . . . ?" Is it possible that I offend? Why not dress up for God anyway? We dress up for man don't we? How can this Style of mine cultivated with such dedication and faithfulness be listed as a depravity? Maybe to use this church of yours for anything, for the paradise your voice evokes, I'll need to repent after all. Which would certainly cost me a third cocktail morality being so chilly and church will turn out expensive.

No. Holiness is no climate for people like me. In time if Monsieur is unable to stop me coming here I may find myself turning over in mind during the sermon not rational certainties like clothes and playmates but abstractions like morality and values. I'll be reduced to the level where I ponder not on interesting problems such as where your personal emotion stops and your divine emotion starts but on metaphysical matters best left alone like where rationalism stops and sentiment starts. Questions with long words like the integration of the personality in the Master-Sentiment could well defeat questions with short words so that I might find myself seeking not some simple, single idea to relate my clothes but some basic formula to integrate life and then what will happen to my appearance?

No the chill of all this archaic morality would certainly cost me too much in Rockets to survive it and I'll seek something cheaper in churches.

Yet where else in this modern Babylon as you call it would

people like me have access to people like you? Where else for that matter would I find anywhere else at all in rue de la Colombe or here the dimension and range of your voice, the dimension and range of your hand, your unsettling How ARE yous, your gratuitous Bless yous and your capacity for injecting heaven? Where would I find this emanation of yours of je ne sais quoi; this "honey'd morphine" never heard tell of in science, bombology, ethics or art, in studios, town halls, church steps or surgeries; this subtle sanctity that comes either from you yourself or is transmitted through you from some unlikely Beyond, challenging what I "absolutely have to" do and warning me of elaborated consequences; these "mystic deliria" of yours suggesting something of the Almighty Delusion for even one moment of your sacred sixty? Where else would I experience this thrilling sense of falling backwards into one permanent grand passion with the most accomplished of Divine Lovers? . . .

ANYWAY . . .

. . . You are preaching quite casually tonight and after last Sunday you need to. You're a man in your late thirties I should say, possibly a clear forty, stop me if I've said this, with no looks by popular standards, by my own standards to be accurate. A healthy unromantic breadth . . . do I detect an hotel waistline there? a reasonable height about what I like, don't overlook these adjectives here; unromantic, healthy, reasonable, everything the maestro isn't. There's nothing physically spectacular about you like Doctor's moonlight for instance . . . say Doctor John to me later . . . nothing picturesque in the line of your clothes like the cheerful drunk on the steps, nothing untidily elegant like Monsieur Montigny and his greens, nothing even spectacularly unspectacular like the hymnbook man at the door, say "hymnbook" to me later. There's only your head well set on your shoulders for anyone susceptible to a forward-set head, and of course all your limbs, there's too many of them, all put on wrongly and too long and your joints clumsily put together, too tall on second thoughts, taller than what I like, and this low brow and so on, closely cut hair like black bristles growing too low down, too close to your brows, there's a word here I won't use, not yet. In all there's nothing there's nothing I can see with my own two eyes to account for the impression gradually growing on me of a certain intangible something, a dignity? Not a tranquillity . . . usual in men of the church; some indefinable emanation a sinner can't learn or acquire not found in the wake of idols but don't let me wander . . .

Where were we now . . . yes. You appear to be casual this evening maybe not in the mood at which I am slightly put out what with someone like me gracing the nave in the pew directly below you. Surely you cannot have overlooked the gleam of my hair which has taken me all day to achieve, the suavity of my line, this indigo creation in . . . now hang on to this point of departure for me I want to return to it . . . this indigo model from the hand of man in precise tubular tailoring, pace-setting, in an original blend of fifty-five per cent orlon (Dupont's acrylic fibre) and forty-five per cent wool, clinging to contour loverlike, the complimentary profile of my shoes by Renaud, my leash-handled bag in calfskin with an ostrich grain by Marcel, and my perfume . . . don't tell me this perfume has not found you . . . the unique Strontium Ninety from an alley on the Left Bank, a fragrance created to heighten and brighten every mood, I don't mean my own, especially meant to rise and guaranteed to rouse . . . now what was my point of departure again? . . . ooh this predatory music. . . .

"In this city of ours," you reflect turning from us, this dark bristly head from the back, "this city of earthquake and blossom," you look out the window near the pulpit and address the tree there, "in this country of New Zealand, this country I might add . . . I MIGHT ADD! . . . which was capable of

47

breeding the man who split the atom, this country which in its both marvellous and dreadful vitality is responsible before God . . ." you ponder upon the tree, stroking your mouth in this way I have come to know as you weigh your words in ones . . . "responsible before God for all that has followed the splitting of the atom, everything from H-bombs to planets . . ." you look in again, pocket your hands and glance at your notes. "I have nothing of this in my notes." You take a turn in the pulpit as though you've forgotten we're here.

"From a country capable of giving the world a lead in nuclear fission, in racial integration, and in social security and, for your information, in case you missed it in the press on Friday, a lead in the Continuous Beer Fermentation Process . . . from a country with this capacity . . . WITH THIS CAPACITY! . . . for originality and drive one might be tempted to look for a lead in the Continuous Love Fermentation Process and in nuclear peace. After all we did start . . . WE DID START! . . . all this." You pause, pondering to yourself then resignedly return to your notes.

With the end plainly in sight what are these last sentences? Maybe I can bear to hear them. . . . "Whereas the mature religious sentiment . . . THE MATURE RELIGIOUS SENTIMENT! . . . includes the work of science as a routine part of God's work. It is the sparkling insight missing from the lifeless ground of science. Love answers questions the rationalist dare not frame. It accommodates every atom of experience referred to it infusing all life with meaning. It is the one thing that integrates the personality. It is what I call the Master-Sentiment.

" 'Let not the wise man glory in his wisdom,
    neither let the mighty man glory in his might,

48

Let not the rich man glory in his riches
but let him that glorieth glory in this;
that he understandeth and knoweth me; that
I am the Lord!
which exercise lovingkindness, judgement and righteousness in the earth: for in these things I delight.' "

Now why is my hand to my mouth? Why the breaking
out of the inner music? The beauty of the voice, the radiance
of the voice? And there was something very like poetry at the
end. Really I must concentrate one of these evenings and
listen to all you say, clumsy and boring though it is. For all
I know you may have been saying something I could make
use of myself. I did hear something about if science had an
answer to sorrow you would post it airmail to the spirit lost in
drink, or in exile. Also I do believe you said something about
the very thing I was thinking about before your voice swept
me away; some basic formula to unify a wardrobe, some
master-sentiment of Style . . . or were you speaking of life?

Is it possible that you yourself could be interesting when
your ponderous sermons are not? Do I detect a personality
here hidden beneath black clothes and grey orthodoxy? One
of these evenings I'd better make an effort to find out what
you say but I'll have to blind myself to your personality first
and deafen myself to your voice for you intercept the word
of the Lord and you take away my vineyards. If only you
preachers knew how to transmit the God you represent rather
than the mere mortals you are. No doubt by now half the
congregation love and the other half hate the all-encom-
passing Master-Sentiment. I anyway reject the man of God
you are supposed to be to consider the man of men. I get over
the feeling in the poetry and remember only the voice that
was speaking it, and far from wondering about the meaning of
this verse sung centuries and centuries ago I'm yet vibrating
beneath the fingers of this voice stilled but a few minutes ago.

It's not the lofty technique of a divine lover that engages me but the low one of a lover mortal. How then can the bewildered sinner find his way through the maze of a human personality to the Master-Seducer beyond it?

I forget to slip out early and am caught by your hand at the door.

I CAN'T GET my dressing done as well these days either; the doctor interrupts me. New Zealand men don't seem to have the faintest idea when to call and when not to. Fancy blowing in on a girl at this holy hour on a Saturday evening when everyone should know she is dressing. How can I prepare for a night of music with Monsieur with an antiseptic doctor in the room? Really this man's technique is debatable.

"I'm dressing, Doctor, you'll notice."

"I don't know that I do notice."

"Oh? Don't you?"

"Doesn't mean a thing to a doctor. Not a thing. Dressing or undressing all women are the same."

"Oh? Fancy . . ."

"No thrill in it for me."

"What a loss."

"Loss? What do you mean?"

"I mean I mean why . . . well . . . why dress at all before a doctor then? Or even undress for that matter. There'd be no point in it at all. Not . . . not that I mean to do either of course." I lend him my eyes a moment. "Not to such an unresponsive audience."

Silence. I take back my eyes. "People like me," I ease the lid from the large cardboard box, "wouldn't dream of wasting good dressing . . . certainly not on a doctor."

Silence again. His teeth close together, I can see them. And what I can hear is his breathing. "So . . . you're dressing." He puts down his bag and takes off his coat, settles in the old low chair and takes out a cigarette. "Don't let me interrupt you . . . Germaine."

I take from their tissue paper the tapered blue pants with the knot of white flowers appliquéd on the seam, and then the white blouse with the same flowers appliquéd on it in blue, unfolding them for the first time since the vendeuse on the rue Royale folded them. "You won't interrupt me Doctor?"

"No."

"Promise?"

Pause . . . then a most unmedical outburst. "How can a man promise anything! . . . with a—a—with a dream like you come true!"

B

ETTER TO SIT in the back I think.

Under the circumstances.

What with three Rockets to get me here, one to encourage me to dress, one to propel me off and a third in the car outside the church to fire me into orbit, well you can see it is simpler to sit at the back. Under these nuclear circumstances I can no longer do credit to Style by sweeping up the aisle to the front. I'll sweep all right but where to and how? The white mohair coat may not be seen to advantage. More comfortable by far to stay at the back, wouldn't you say so too mon cher?

There are evenings when I'm obliged to break the law up to three or four times on the way to this place of worship, swerving through the maze of traffic regulations, sorting out the coloured lights at intersections and trying to work out how many cars I see coming, not to mention the very strict one about the drinking driver. Don't the authorities of Babylon want me to perform what I call my devotions arranging all these difficulties in the way? It would be a good idea to meet the magistrate socially first of my own free will before I have to meet him legally. There must be surely some pockets of forgiveness in magistrates and ministers as well as in the Lord if I could only discover them in time, before consequences catch up I mean, now where was I again? . . .

Ye-es . . . walking up the aisle. All this has a bearing on how I walk up the aisle which simply means that I don't walk up at all. I sit in the back and I mean the back. I don't presume to use a pew. I pirate the chair of the hymnbook man barely within the door while he is standing and singing God's praises. Let him reflect on my breath in a pew. He hasn't the occasion for this chair that I have. He can have it back when I am demoted to listening at the door with the drunk.

Fortunately I am now much farther away from your pulpit what with my mounting consequences. It is now a longer and safer distance over the grey heads of the congregation at the back, the smart hats of some new ones in the middle and the eloquent empty pews at the front, to you who precipitate all this, and well it needs to be. I can no longer endure to be closer, I am beginning to suspect a not inconsiderable element of plain instinctive man behind your plausible standing in for God. Which may be you would think a wrong sort of suspicion to bring into an house of holiness and one that should be kept in the rear of any church if not well out in the foyer. With all of which I agree since your possible virility confuses the issue of what I have actually come for and I'm confused enough as it is, now there's an involved paragraph have I finished it? . . .

I'm no longer sure what I come for. Every Sunday I try to stop it and Monsieur trains the best of his brains upon it, lyricism, poetry and all. I heard in this very church that this is the place where order and felicity are accessible to all yet what do I find but chaos? I achieve more felicity after an hour of music with Monsieur than after an hour in church with a minister; it would have been more in the interests of order this evening to have called in Doctor John to prescribe me his brand of felicity than to have sought this infelicitous chastity, arousing the very passions it professes to restrain. Doctors can be not bad at felicity at all, nearly as accomplished as music masters and miles better than ministers; so cheerfully soulless I've found them, leaving their souls home with their wives. Felicity of the kind I mean can be damn good fun without the sweat of a soul; souls can be such a complication don't you think? But you promised not to let me wander. . . .

Anyway . . .

. . . your voice still reaches me, the sound of it at least, if not the inelegant sentences, the laboured argument and the overcharged sentimentality. But I'm afraid it would wherever I sat. Whatever you say as an expert in morality, in whatever language you say it and whatever the meaning intended your voice would reach me were I sitting at the back of the world which in this country I probably am.

I could never follow any argument tonight though even did I wish to. Nuances of thought and ingredients of Rockets never combined in me. Besides once the suspicion of being taught takes over I hopelessly lose the place and leave the whole thing to the Christians. All I want is the sensation of your voice and never mind meaning and purpose. . . .

Not that I look at you often. For one thing you may be looking at me which even three Rockets cannot support, and for another once I do lift my eyes to your travelling dark ones it is as much as I can do to lower them again. And what girl is fool enough to reveal anything she can avoid revealing to either God or man? After sampling both looking and not looking I find it more comfortable not to. Just hang on to this

55

disputed chair within the door, thoroughly late, thoroughly inflamed, thoroughly bewitched and relax in a moment of heaven. . . .

. . . I should be more careful slipping out of church doors during last hymns on account of accruing consequences. Have I embarrassed this drunk or can't you embarrass drunks? "You should have remembered my ways," I whisper.

"You should have remembered mine."

I creep across the porch. "I never seem to be able to see these services out."

"I can't even see them in."

I reach the nearest stone seat. He lays a hand upon the stone back picturesquely of course. "Enter the Villain," profoundly.

"You don't convince me." Three cocktails last for an hour and cancel all preliminaries. Ooh the lovely cool air on my face! Freedom, coolness, reality. The wonderful world of the understandable and tangible: bitumen, metal, wood, stone, leaves, flowers and the jukebox down the street. "I need this cigarette mon Dieu!" The last hymn is surging from the church arm in arm with the jukebox tune. God and Baal must be pals in these parts.

"You don't convince me either," he says.

"I get the impression you are only playing the drunkard and not so very well either."

"I get the impression you are only playing the Christian and that not very well either."

"If it were not for your breath, mon cher scélérat, I'd doubt if you were drunk at all."

"If it were not for your presence here I'd doubt you were a Christian at all."

56

"Why don't you make up your own sentences instead of copying mine?"

"My own would be far too original; you'd barely understand a word."

I laugh. From the hard stone seat I take a closer look at him. Faces are really hard to see in this complicated light. In the shadow of the hat brim there appears to be too much white to the eyes or the irises have been painted too dark or the sockets too hollowed out, something cadaverously wrong unless the shadows mislead me. But he does seem too stagey to be genuine, even the beard looks a glued-on job. "Oh well," I yawn, "you must excuse me. I have a most pressing appointment." I rise and go and take my seat in the car and he drapes himself over the bonnet. "But *I* am a most pressing appointment."

"Ooh you outright New Zealander!"

We both laugh like anything drowning the hymn and the jukebox. "Well I've still got an appointment."

"I'm astonished that anyone could leave *me*."

"You bore me that's why."

"I mean to. I'm tired of being interesting."

"Quite a good answer." The engine is running softly and other cars are swooping by. People pass by too hurrying sadly somewhere as if hurry ever paid. If it did I'd be hurrying to Monsieur.

"I regret I've achieved something good if only an adequate answer."

I play with the key.

He tries to stand upright. "I must return to my stone seat. I'm being too lavish with my wit." I forget Monsieur waiting at his German grand across the road. "It's about all you can be lavish with in this country of import controls," he adds. "Why don't you laugh at that? That's fearfully funny."

I do.

"But forgive me for amusing you, I can't always help it. Leave the engine on."

I switch it off.

"Exit the villain in your life." Have you noticed how cocktails and sermons end up in yawns? Especially both together. I notice his long fingers moving; authentically and not acted. "Will you," he asks, "tell me something I've been wondering for weeks?"

"We all wonder for weeks."

"Why, have you been wondering for weeks?"

"Weeks and weeks and weeks."

"Why *do* you come to church?"

"Ooh . . . that?"

"Your eyes make a man want to tell you everything; compel him to uncover his entire soul."

"Ooh you men and your souls!"

" 'Sulky lips shaped for sin . . .' "

"The church and I differ on the meaning of sin."

"Why do you come to church?"

"To wear my clothes of course."

"Don't you get anything from the preacher at all?"

"Indeed I do! His voice addresses my entire physique. My organs! They stand up and change places. I . . ."

"Exactly which organs?" His voice is earnest. "I was always one who liked my details correct. I . . ."

"I don't know what you mean. Now I must . . ."

"You know exactly what I mean."

"I do not."

"You do so."

"I don't."

"You do."

"Your originality is running away with you. You ask questions nice people shouldn't."

" 'Kiss me right, kiss me wrong!' " wails the jukebox.

"Kissing must end," he says, "some day . . . Gomer. Think of the emotional dilapidation then . . . the vineyards laid waste."

"I don't care if it does. There are plenty of playmates."

"What will happen to your soul when the kissing has to stop?"

"I haven't got a soul. I've only got a solar plexus."

"Are you asking me to believe there is no soul behind those eyes?"

"Not so far Villain." Suddenly the inner music breaks through and it is no longer the music I know. It is the music of a voice I know, ranging and descending, beating birdlike, injecting l'amour . . . I brush my eyes. "I beg your pardon what did you say?"

"You're listening to something. What do you hear? You're always doing it."

"I'm listening to you of course."

"You told me before that was your secret infirmity."

"What's wrong with a secret infirmity? All the best people have them."

"Do they?"

"Besides I was listening to you."

"No you were not."

"Yes I was."

"You were not."

"I was so. I know exactly what you were talking about. You were talking about . . . about . . ."

"I was talking about the soul."

"I've been hearing too much about souls these days, from ministers and music masters and now from a villain. Have you wretches got nothing else on your minds? Souls are indecent and on no account should they be mentioned. They always spoil the fun."

"Isn't that disastrous."

"Ooh drop this revolting subject." I light up another cigar- ette. "You tell me something *I've* been wondering for weeks."

"I will with pleasure Gomer."

"You leave Gomer in the Old Testament!"

He laughs. I offer him a cigarette. "What brings *you* to church?"

"A maid in the second row of the choir, right on the end at the left."

"On the right."

"On the left. On her left anyway."

"By the pulpit? That pure-eyed thing?"

"If I could only touch that maid . . . I would no longer need to drink for oblivion. I could lose myself in the greatest of grand passions."

"Not really."

"I can't stand consciousness. Have you a lighter? Thanks. Drink is a bit expensive for oblivion. Every now and again I've got to work for the funds. Grand passion shouldn't cost anything like it."

"Ooh you're making all this up."

"Oblivion . . . death in an endless kiss. No trace, no outline, no shadow of the anguished moments of truth."

"Even for you the kissing will have to stop and then what will happen to *your* soul?"

"The kissing *I* start will never stop."

"Mon Dieu!"

"Kissing for the fun of it like yours will stop but kissing for the hell of it won't."

"You unnerve me Villain."

"For me the end will never come."

"You're better than the Old Testament."

"I wrote the Old Testament."

"I don't know why I go into church at all with someone like you out here. I'll stay outside next time."

"All I need is to touch that maid; to touch her unawares."

"Well why in the name of le Grand Dieu don't you come to, spruce yourself up, unglue those whiskers, drop the disguise and join her after church one night? L'amour is progressive you must know."

"It would not I believe progress."

"Why not? What are you like under that hat?"

"To be frank I'm remarkably handsome."

"Not really?"

"I'm the ideal man. Once this maid saw me as I really am she would at once surrender and I would lose this heaven of longing. No all I mean to do is touch her unawares so that it remains I who do the surrendering."

"Well it's all very involved but aa . . . it makes a rattling good story. It tells well," I add. "Now I really must make a move." He takes a cigarette from my case and I offer him my lighter. It fails to go and I find the box of matches. "I must join that compatriote of mine. This hymn must . . . MUST! . . . aren't capital letters catching? . . . must be nearing the end."

"Like kissing even hymns must end." He draws on his cigarette hungrily and leans both elbows on the sill. No one would need a gin with his breath as close as this. "You are one of these luxurious creatures who . . ." "How do you know." "By the gold in your teeth."

"Why, haven't you got gold in your teeth?"

"Not so far."

"All good Babylonians grow gold in their teeth. It's the only jewellery I wear."

"You must be a very good Babylonian."

"That's what I thought till I came to this church. But the Reverend Guymer thinks otherwise."

"Oh that chap in there! That vain self-dramatising actor . . . that ineffective half-inch man . . . what is he trying to prove?"

"Is that what you think of him?"

"Why what do you think of him?"

"I don't think I don't listen."

He is shivering softly and esoterically. Is it cold out there? But there's a little more cadence in his voice now engendering a little more life. I prefer cadence and life in my playmates don't you? Easier than secret souls. His age . . . I could give him a year or two or that's what I think in this light. "There must be," I say, "all of twenty-six or twenty-seven verses to that hymn in there with eight or nine lines to each." But the inner music of your voice breaks through. What's happened to the G Flat Impromptu that accompanied me to church? I'd rather have my Impromptu. What terrible thing has happened to me that your voice should be the music? I must get Monsieur to play me the G Flat several times over the minute I arrive to put it back in the auditorium of my mind. Put it back where it was when I came here. I'll not suffer your voice within me . . . I brush it all away from my eyes. "So sorry what were you saying?"

"Just watching your listening eyes."

"I thought you were saying something."

"I was only watching your eyes listening and wondering what to."

"Please don't talk about that."

"Have you noticed," one finger lifts from the others on the sill and taps for the time that a couple walks by then it stops and rests with the others and he speaks in a voice that is normal and no longer theatrical. He goes on just like one young person gossiping easily with another, "Have you noticed there have been more at church lately? A few more. See these extra cars?" No lavish wit sparkling or otherwise, no more old-fashioned villain striving after effect. He's shivering but he's real and convincing in simplicity. I answer "So there are more cars."

I'm never anxious to leave youth for middle age even this drunk, shivering, laconic twenty for an overadoring forty. Here comes another yawn each and here is the engine still running softly and patiently an undertone to our talk yet I don't slip in the clutch. "There are some others in the middle pews these nights, younger people with smart hats and men with their hair actually cut."

"I wonder," yawn, "why. There's that hymn over at last, only the benediction left."

"And the sound of his step down the aisle beneath the congregation singing Amen. I like that part and hate missing it."

"I'm going back to my stone seat. Tonight might be the time. She may walk near enough to touch."

"There's the benediction. 'May the Lord keep you' and so on. I must go. I might get caught by that hand. Goodnight Villain. Any cars coming? Au revoir. May l'amour progress."

"Goodnight Gomer. May the kissing never stop."

I could do with an whole page here, mon cher, as I drive up the main street giving the Christians time to go home before I join Monsieur Montigny. An whole page, even a chapter, sitting in my car beneath the tall clock tower rearing white into the dark evening like the illustrious princess of Jerusalem; swishing her skirts over the railway line that cuts Babylon in half below. I could do with an whole pageful receiving the sounds of a Sunday night city above the undersong of your voice; a breather to settle the ingredients of you men within me before I stir in the next. But I must not be later than I am. People like me don't like hurrying but people like him don't like waiting. Besides I might bore you, mon cher, as you have often bored me if I start preaching about the whispering of long cars rising to the crossing and sliding over and on; the voices of bodgies and widgies at corners laughing and talking and whistling; the drooling and squealing of a jukebox; the grunts of shunting at the station nearby; the high urgent call of a coming rail car; lovers' lowered voices together on the seats at the base of the Tower and ever the clop clip clop of shoes on the pavement of people hurrying somewhere till the Clock Tower strikes the half-hour . . .

. . . but I'd better wheel round to Monsieur and make a paragraph do.

> "Pour engloutir mes sanglots apaisés
> Rien ne me vaut l'abîme de ta couche;
> L'oubli puissant habite sur ta bouche
> Et le Léthé coule dans tes baisers."

"What is my life but waiting!"

Look at Monsieur raving in his authentic Paris style. I stand within the doorway of his studio in my white coat full of admiration. It's like old times to see this sort of thing. You get a lot of it in the rue de la Colombe but nothing to touch it here. I stand feeling the warmth of the panelled room after the cool of the city's spring night; with still a little of the villain I have just left within me and still a little of you; I am a long-stemmed glass holding the ingredients of men within me. Listen to this one here! Look at the wide generous face flashing with everything it's got to flash with and his voice touching all its registers. What a comprehensive rage. Look at him flinging his hands and thumping them on the table rattling the glasses and rocking the decanter! Look out there goes a . . . "Waiting for pupils! Waiting for audiences! Waiting for recognition in France! Waiting for fulfilment in my work, waiting for love and waiting for you! When are life's promises to be kept!" Thump again on the table; a round sound that doesn't hurt.

Don't his eyes look alive when he's raging; bigger and brighter and greyer. The full features, the full mouth, they

64

look their best in action. I love to see a man in action; one always sees a man at his best when he's extended, I think. They . . . "Is this waiting another of life's furnaces! How many more furnaces has life for me! Is the steel of me not yet tempered! Am I not yet pure after these years of testing! In . . . out . . . and sharpened on the grindstone! In . . . out . . . and sharpened! In . . . out . . . sharpened! My sensibility would shame a razor blade!" This is how you should improvise from the pulpit and ditch those dreary notes. Then we'd listen like anything. Oh but this is a good story; a very very good story; easily as good as Gomer. It's got the same . . .

"I know the inside of a furnace! Mon Dieu, I know the furnace! I know its icy-white heat! I know its snow-white coals! . . . and the blazing white of its agonies! Why have *you* been sent to torture me! Why has this beauty exploded before me! For inspiration? For fulfilment? For love? *Speak!* Or are you another white furnace! . . . *Speak!* Why do you wear white tonight! What are you to me but a slender white voluptuous agony! Speak, Torment, *speak!*"

"I've a cerise frock beneath."

A moment of crisis . . . *thump!* and his voice lifts a tone. "She wears cerise beneath!" He holds his mighty breath a moment in further exciting crisis then strides across the room to the piano and *crash!* with both fists on the keys.

I wince badly. "Don't do that," I warn.

He turns slowly, crouching, whispering. "Don't do that, you say. Don't do that. Don't make any noise that might offend your slender white ear. Don't inconvenience one who claims to be sensitive to sound. Don't expose her secret infirmity. But how insupportably pathetic!" Suddenly a shout in my face. "What about *my* sensitivity! What about *my* white hells! What about *my* secret infirmity! Does it matter that *I* am sensitive to waiting! That *you* inconvenience *me!*"

"Monsieur, the course of your emotion is too conventional.

You hardly do credit to France. Pray improvise something original. Even the man in the pulpit . . ."

"Where is my first recital tonight but put aside for you! The series I've arranged for you. Where are the audiences I need for my work but turned away for you! A notice in the foyer: 'Monsieur Montigny will not be performing tonight!' He's engaged on something more important! He's waiting . . . waiting . . . *waiting!*" Boom . . . boom . . . boom . . .

"Hurry is bad for people like me."

"Mon Dieu! Is that all you have to say!" He tears out a cigarette from a pocket and all but swallows it. Then snatches it out again. "Wallowing in that miasma of sanctified sensuality across the road because hurry is bad for people like you!" He swings round to the table and pours wine in a glass. I say, look at him pouring it all over his papers too . . . hooh! into his mouth and down his throat. "Be careful, Léon. Don't spill anything on that suit; it's the only green one in town."

His grey eyes widen in disbelief, his full mouth opens, his whole wide generous face is a canvas of disbelief. Then everything closes and narrows and he creeps forward again whispering. "So you do value something in me."

"On you, Monsieur, on you." I yawn; isn't it dreadful? I can't possibly control it. Don't forget, mon cher, that I have had three Rockets and two soul-shows already which never fail to breed yawns. He studies this yawn following it with interest right through all its stages to the finish; a rumbling within him like a coming volcano then suddenly he wheels back to the piano and *crash!* with both hands on the keys.

I lift my gloved hands to my breasts. "I told you not to do that."

Crash! both hands on the bass.

"You wouldn't do that if my father were here."

Crash! Crash! Crash! . . . for the length of the shivering keyboard. Treble and bass in inspired cacophony knifing and slaying the air. I press my hands to my breasts where it seems to get me worst. It occurs to me for the first time to believe the Montigny scandal in Paris fifteen years ago: that it could be true what they said about Léon Montigny. I think this man *could* be a monster. I let go the breath I am holding and speak softly to him as he stands holding down the keys. "Léon you are the only person in New Zealand who knows what happened when I was born. The only one who understands how I feel about sound; the only one who happens to know why. And yet you can do this to me."

The uproar that comes from the German grand I wish you could hear, mon cher. Indeed you may hear it, for that matter. If you can hear it over there across the city in your orderly quiet parsonage it will give you an idea of what the nuclear fission you preach about is like. Suddenly I cave in and flop in the armchair and stiffen all over and hold my body everywhere. "I'll write to my father," I say, "and tell on you. I'll cable him tomorrow morning."

He flings to his knees beside me. I can smell the tweed and the wine on him, the man odour and the sweat. "What have I done," he moans. "Oh Grand Dieu what have I done. Oh my love, my love, what have I done. Oh my dearest, forgive me."

"I'll never forgive you!"

"Oh my darling you must forgive me or I'll die. You must understand my Gethsemane. If only you could sympathise a little. If you could only know what it is to be waiting hour after hour on end and listening for a step that's dear. Forgive me, ma chère Germaine, you must."

"I'll cable my father tomorrow morning!"

His arms take me. "I know about your birth Germaine. I know all about your babyhood. Your father told me. In the rue de la Colombe in the vine-covered cottage with the bistro on the ground floor. I lived near Notre-Dame too. I understand all that. But," his arms release me, "you brought this on yourself. You tortured me in your own way, in the Parisian way."

"I'll tell my father on you!"

"Don't shake like that Germaine." He grasps my hands. Don't I can't stand it! You must think of *me* and of how *I* feel. I've had enough hell for one night. Don't upset me any further. You don't know what an evening I've had of grinding pulverising waiting. Don't shake like that Germaine! I'll give you some wine. It'll soothe you." He hurries away ridiculously and pours it and brings it. "It'll mend the sore places ma chère.

"Tell me what I can do. I'll do anything if you'll forgive me . . . good girl, another sip . . . I'll teach you day and night. I'll make you the most celebrated performer in Europe. I'll transplant the whole of my own heart and soul and agonies into the sensational brilliance of your fingers so that no one will know it is not yours. Good girl, drink some more. Good, soon you'll be all right. I'll do anything that you might forgive me. Now this last bit . . . good girl. Now stop shaking sweetheart. Let me smooth your beautiful face . . . these exquisite listening eyes." The handkerchief smells of him as he smooths away the powder with it and I see the lipstick on it. Now he cups my face in his hands searching all over it, probing deeply in my eyes, searching, probing, examining. "I'll do anything Germaine if you'll forgive me. I'm prepared to do anything at all. Do you know what I'm thinking of now? Do you? Can't you guess?" He touches my chin with his mouth and rises and walks to the keyboard and lays a lovely major chord upon the keys. "We'll marry, Germaine" . . . and holds it there standing . . . "and soon."

"Who said!"

He hangs on to the chord and replies with pain and patience. "I am saying it now." He lifts his fingers to the same chord again. "We'll marry Germaine and soon. Faute de mieux."

"That's what you think!"

"It is what I know." The chord takes some of his impatience. "Really but the child in you can be exasperating!" His chords announce this exasperation. "Will I never touch the woman in you."

"I'd never marry a monster!"

He leaves the keyboard and looks for cigarettes tapping his pockets. "Don't use that word of me."

"You've used worse of me."

"I don't know what I used. I never remember afterwards."

"You called me a white furnace."

"Did I . . . oh? Many a woman would be proud to be called that by me." He lights a cigarette.

"I'm not many a woman."

"White furnace . . . did I truly?" He draws the smoke appreciatively.

"I'm just an ordinary girl and . . ."

"That's for me to say."

". . . and I'd never marry a monster like you."

"You know that I'm not a monster. You must allow genius elbow room. I'm not a monster by any means."

"Yes you are!"

"I say I'm *not!*"

"They all said on the Left Bank you were!"

He studies his cigarette a moment standing near the piano and watches the smoke rising. "That wretch took her own life. The Court proved she did."

"The Court couldn't prove that *you* did. Everybody knows that you . . ."

Softly: "I wouldn't advise you to rouse me on that."

"Ooh I don't want to talk about it!"

"Neither do I." Pause. "The law didn't sentence me but life did."

"I don't want to talk about Paris at all. I want to forget for a time. I've got things to forget too. I've come out here for a . . . for an adagio, after the opening movement of my life." I say no more. My breasts and other places are still sore from the onslaught of cacophony especially the solar plexus but I can't get at that to hold. He moves easily across the carpet and half-sits upon the table and speaks in another voice. "You know that I didn't mean this Germaine. I never remember

what I've said when I . . . or what I've done when I . . .
these—these orgasms of rage come upon me like a visitation,
like tornados from the Pacific when the suffering is too, too
. . . you know how I suffer in this clumsy country, dropping
and breaking its way through socialism. Its banalities mon
Dieu! Its heavy-footed mentality, its factory-cut morality and
its gaudy way of life, the humiliation of it! To have to teach
its limited hands to play an instrument with the limitless
range of a pianoforte, to have to remain within its blundering
reach. Day in day out, year in year out, cringing from every
contact, and then for you to appear!" A deep man-deep sigh.
"*You!*" He lays the butt in an ash tray and a hand covers his
eyes. "Chic, soignée, à la mode. All white and gold and blue-
eyed like the Spring herself in person, like Paris herself in
bloom. All this magic about you . . . this feeling you give a
man that heaven is real. This look in your eyes that radiates
glamour upon all that happens to be near, upon the very
pavement beneath your feet. This extraordinary sense of
miracle you cast that blots out all but the wonder." He stands
and returns to the keyboard. "We'll marry Germaine," the
chords I hear supply a fair idea of what he feels about it, "and
soon. I've had enough of le plaisir clandestin."

"I'll marry again but not you. My father said I was to marry
my own age next time."

"Age has no traffic with l'amour."

"L'amour has no traffic with me."

"L'amour will come when I touch the woman. The woman
in you is still virgin. You'll marry me and soon." The chords
have lost their intones of exasperation and are back to their
initial conviction, a soft confidence. The sound of them is a
tender ointment to people like me whatever their emotional
source. My poor breasts feel better. "In time," he says, "I'll
be necessary to you." The chords rise in transition. "If I am
not that already now."

"Only a kind man can ever be necessary to me. As un-
selfish as Raoul."

"Only children talk of kindness. I'm talking of l'amour." They rise developing through the minor, rise in crescendo knitting together the jagged edges he has so recently torn, soothing them like fragrant lotion; wine was never like this. "Kindness has nothing to do with l'amour as men know it my child. What do *kind* men know of la grande passion?"

"That's for me to say."

. . . rising in thrilling progression to a tall triumphant major. "The twentieth century owes this to me: we'll marry Germaine and soon!"

He opens the clasp of my white coat. "What are you wearing for me my heart? Cerise . . ." He touches the peau de soie with its plunging décolletage .. . . "A cerise sheath beneath." His eyes close. "Oh mon Dieu . . . 'le divin opium . . .'"

I stir and sit upright. "Give me some more of that wine Léon." I investigate the state of my hair. "I feel better now." I watch the green-clad form humbling and anxiously pouring my wine not spilling any this time taking the greatest care. Can't you men be pathetic? Especially when you're in the heart's confessional. But I never was one for pathos. Didn't I say somewhere that souls were complicating? I meant to. If only we could close this embarrassing scene. If only he would make me smile! Think of all those loud laughs that impossible drunkard gave me, that ridiculous moustache and beard. Sandwiched in between you and Léon he made a delightful savoury filling. He's the one ingredient that saves the cocktail. "Thank you so much Léon." I take a long deep drink. At least I can help myself along with wine during this soul-parade as I can't very well in church. I feel considerably better and lift one leg over the other . . . discreetly; the radioactive line is hazardous.

"You recall to me," he says, "the Deux Magots."

"The Deux Magots is touristy now. The beards have long since moved to more off-beat pastures." I glance up. "I suppose my face is pretty bad."

71

"I've seen it pretty bad before."

"Do I need to fix it at this late hour?"

"I can survive it."

We both smile and I glance up at him over the rim of my glass. His wide grey eyes with traces still of the recent storm and a gleam of smile mixed in them, his eyes looking down upon me are, what's the word . . . interesting. One end of his mouth confirms the smile in his eyes and lifts a little. "I still like compatriotes," I offer.

"Do you?"

"Yes."

"Have you got over . . . all that?"

"I don't mind your rages."

"Don't you?"

"As long as you don't . . . do *that* again."

"You have forgiven me?"

I still look up over the rim of my glass at him. Silent.

"Sweetheart?"

I look up, still look up at him.

"My dearest love?"

Silence.

"Have you?"

"Of course."

"You have?"

I finish the remainder of my wine and place the glass on the floor, "Yes," and lie back with eyes closed. But there's a risk in lying back with eyes closed. The inner music breaks through and floods forward and it is still the music of your voice ranging and beating from the pulpit in superb winging and grounding. I gaze upward listening wide-eyed . . . "Whoredom and wine taketh away the heart my people and we have gone a-whoring from under our God." I try to close my mind against it. There are some deep pitfalls in your church mon cher. I'll be catching your damned religion if I'm not careful without ever hearing a thing. You're taking something from me, you're taking away my vineyards, my peace of mind. "I will lay waste her vines and fig trees." You're doing something to me that is bad for my famous serenity. Your whole service is one grand pitfall with you yourself digging it. I keep on losing my head in church all the time without stopping. What is this nebulous danger? I can't put my finger on anything to resist. By comparison Léon's rages are table talk. It's like some kind of villain in my life, some great big almighty intangible villain that my young drunkard was talking about. He knew what he . . . ooh the music of your voice! I brush my eyes roughly . . . "I beg your pardon . . . what were you saying?"

"I was saying Come back Germaine. You've listened long enough."

"There are some deep pitfalls in that church Monsieur."

"You leave the church where it belongs across the road. You are here with me Germaine."

"What were we talking about before?"

"Don't you remember what I was saying to you?"

"Was it important?"

"Mon Dieu you raise inconsequence to the height of an art Madame de Beauvais!"

"I just want to know what we were talking about. People like me like to come back to their points."

"Have you got the matches?" He lights a cigarette. "You were saying you had forgiven me." He approaches and lifts a knee on the arm of my chair and looks down on me with concentration. "You must think of *me* while you're here."

I laugh, I shouldn't. "I am compatriote and it's no trouble either. And I was thinking of you yesterday at practise." I close my eyes again and murmur, "I don't know why you don't ditch all your silly pupils Léon and get on with your composition."

"Il faut tenter de vivre."

"I'll keep you. I've got plenty of money. Why not squander

some of my royalties for me?" I lift my eyelids enough to see how he is taking it. "What will you have it in; francs, dollars or sterling?" Then lower them again. "It's great fun," I add, ". . . or marks or kroner?"

He kneels and lays his head upon me. I feel it heavy and my body curves in beneath it. I look at the hair so near; curly, uncut, and untidy yet still elegant and . . . interesting. Is that a grey hair or two? I like the close odour of a man. The first odour that met me when I was born and laid in my father's arms, and that stayed with me constantly through childhood. I have this natural inclination for and trust in and preference for men, knowing only men all my life. Men are my true habitat. If ever I so far forgot myself as to breed I'd only keep the sons. I take my cigarettes from my coat pocket, the matches from Monsieur's and light up luxuriously. People like us understand each other better when we are touching bodily somewhere. It amounts to a physical guarantee of good faith like your church-door handshake and considerably more convincing. "Ditch all your damned pupils, Léon. Get on with composition. Finish the 'Bridges of Paris.' It's a gloriously lovely chanson. It's small . . . small; but in it, I think, you have the germs of a complete sonata. If you would only relax enough to develop it. I'll give your work a premiere performance . . . a world premiere . . . when I return to Europe. Always supposing that by then you will have succeeded in translating into my cold technique your own hot heart and soul. Then you can return from exile and wallow in your own glory." I pause a moment to recall the "Bridges of Paris" but here is your voice instead. ". . . but let him that glorieth glory in this; that he understandeth and knoweth me . . ." I lay an alarmed hand on his head. "There are some deep pitfalls in that church, Monsieur!"

"Come back Germaine. Remember you are here with me." He stirs and finally stands. "Just rise a little. Let me take this coat right off, take the white right away, ah . . .

74

that's better. This cerise has light within it. There must be light in you that you should glow outwardly so. There must be some warmth in you. There must be a heart in your gossamer body for your face to be shaped like one. I'll find that heart some day. If I have to tear open your body and search every corner of it, I'll find that heart some day. And when I do, even if it turns out to be the size of a sapphire, I'll take it out and put it in a flowerpot and nurture it with all the feminine maternal care that I know has been denied it until it grows a normal size then I'll put it back in the place where it should be and where at the moment it is not. So that one day I'll hear you say 'Je t'aime.' Oh but just to look at you, to look at you is enough. To see you just as you are. At times even this is too much. The full quota of joy in a man's life is meant to be dispersed but all mine concentrates in this moment. What does it matter whether you can love or not? You're too lovely to be endured. You are sheet lightning in my brain."

I brush my eyes. "I beg your pardon . . . what were you saying?"

Crisis. He covers his face.

"Sorry, Léon."

Silence. Only the whir of the traffic. Dulled through the concrete distance. A gasp of pain: "Your eyes looked as though you were listening to me."

"I'm fearfully sorry, Léon. You know I can't help it. I was hearing someone . . . I mean something else." The ingredients of you two men within me can hardly be said to mix.

But he still stands in silence with his hands pressed to his face so that I find in myself a faint inkling of what it must be like to kill a man. And I don't like this inkling, I tell you. "Forgive me, Léon. Léon? Mon cher?" I reach up and touch the hands on his face. "I forgave you," I whisper, "for something much worse than this. Mon cher ami? Mon cher compatriote? I forgave you for your infirmity; cannot you then forgive mine?" I gently pull away the hands and smile up at him with everything I've got, leaning forward below him. Suddenly, disastrously, he snatches me. "Mon coeur . . ."

"No wait, wait, Léon. I want you to play to me first. Please I . . ."

"Mon coeur . . ."

"You must wait! You must play to me first Léon! I want you to play me the G Flat. I . . . please play me the . . ."

"Your perfume . . . it makes me . . ."

"Wait! You must play me the . . . wait!"

"Do you know what you are saying?"

"The G Flat?"

"Recall your last word . . . recall it!"

"Ooh . . . you mean 'wait'?"

"Promise never to use that word to me again!"

"Ooh . . . I forgot."

"Promise me!"

"I promise you. I promise you Léon. But I do beg you to play to me for a while. I . . . I've got a special reason I . . . an absolutely-have-to reason . . . you know what your music does to me. I . . . it does all the things to me that . . . that you say my eyes do to you. I . . . it might make me say 'Je t'aime.' "

"Will it . . ."

I touch his mouth with mine, no more than a touch.

"You'll . . ." he labours, "you'll . . . have to . . . play it to me instead. "Your mouth . . . 'me ravit en extase . . .' "

"Not me, I've had too much to drink. I've arrived at the inconsequent stage."

"You need more wine my heart. I can't abide so inconclusive a stage."

I move over to the second chair at the pianoforte and there take my glass from him. "Have you got the matches?" I *must* exorcise your voice from within me. I want nothing of you within me. Even something so intangible as a voice . . . I

76

can't stand you two men within me; the ingredients collide with each other.

. . . Yet when the Impromptu is over and the descending diminishing chords fade out upon the air I can still hear your damned voice clearly; so do all my glands and arteries and marrows and plexus so that when Monsieur turns to me, turns to me, unloading his soul upon me I am all too ready to try passion then and no longer tell him to wait. But he says in my throat, "I've got something for you Germaine. I completed it this evening." The drum and the whine of the muffled traffic . . . "I'll play it to . . ."

"No . . . not now . . . not yet . . ."

"I'll play it to you first."

"Don't go . . ."

"First, Germaine . . . first."

"Don't stop . . ."

But he does and he turns once more to the keys and I hear his notes as he gropes for the place. "It is a chanson called . . ."

"Come back Léon."

". . . called 'Waiting' . . ."

"I want you . . . to come back . . ."

". . . dedicated to you."

"No . . ." I reach over and stay his hands; the drone and the hum and the whine and the drum of the . . . He grips my hands. "We'll go to Three Trees . . . I'll play it there . . . afterwards."

"Um . . ."

"We'll go . . . now."

I no longer hear your voice, just the wonderful sound of the traffic out in the dark night city filling up the background of my mind. Then the sharp sound of a rising siren, bitter, urgent.

"Germaine . . . come . . . we'll go now."

But the siren soars hysterically and the fires in me go out. "What did you say?" The passion in me goes out . . . but only in me.

"We'll go to Three Trees . . . I'll play it afterwards . . . Germaine . . ."

"But can you drive?"

"You can."

"I can't drive your car."

"Then drive yours."

"But what about yours? How will you get home?"

"Then drive mine."

"But your clutch and gears come out of the floor. I have no idea how to . . ."

"Then drive yours."

"But how will you . . ."

"*Transport!* . . . *Transport!* . . . at a moment like this!" He jerks back his chair and is on his feet. "Fiddling little mechanical metal details at a moment like this! Clutches and gears and floors when the blood of my life is about to be offered in immortal chanson! The world premiere of my suffering. And you can drool on about the workings of cars and who is to drive and how one gets home!" He raises clenched fists high above him. "Mon Dieu, Madame de Beauvais! This is . . ."

"Now don't you hit those keys!"

". . . positively insupportable!" *Crash!* on the wall beside him.

"But I don't even know where your brakes are. I need brakes at the inconsequent stage. *Somebody's* got to . . ."

"*Stop* . . . *it* . . . *!* Pour l'amour de Dieu!"

As-tu quelquefois respiré
Avec ivresse et lente gourmandise
Ce grain d'encens qui remplit une église . . . ?

T HE REVEREND GUYMER is reading from Hosea again, thirty centuries back. For some reason you have interrupted your campaign on the Master-Sentiment introduced some Sundays ago leaving the intricate argument of it for Hosea's warm temperament. Do you think we could do with a little forgiveness or could you yourself do with a little tenderness? I don't know why but whenever you read Hosea to us I feel you are personally speaking to me; a disputable and uncomfortable feeling deep in the area of sentiment that you claim is unchartered. . . . In any case you are gentle tonight.

True, the text could well accommodate an occasional sforzando if not an outright cadenza and could I think have drained away something of the pent-up rivers I'm beginning to suspect within you but you do not avail yourself of it. Are you for the time being no longer pent up or has your grand passion for God, a woman or an idea achieved some temporary release in a way unknown to us? a thought I don't want to hold. But whatever the source of this gentleness the congregation is gratefully relaxed; a surely growing congregation I note with young heads added to the grey.

Is it possible that for one evening at least you see some good in us? By now everyone knows both within the church and out, not to mention within the press and out, that whenever God is rebuking his people Israel it is really the Reverend Guymer rebuking his people in the City; notorious as we are for burning incense to graven images the work of our own hands and a-whoring from under our God. Are we for one short hour reprieved? Is this the fragrance of forgiveness that ministers and magistrates are short of? What say we all take heart? I anyway feel not unlike the faithless Gomer when her husband allured her into the wilderness, spoke tenderly to her and gave her back her vineyards. In the palace of my youth I sing.

"Hear the word of the Lord as it is contained in the book of Hosea," you say.

You look carefully around all our faces to see if we are going to hear it. The church lighting makes your features look—remote—as the street lighting does outside. And the voluminous academic gown removes any shape from the rest of you. I haven't yet seen you in daylight. But I'm beginning to detect with a little more conviction your emanation of a persistent dignity, if not a suspect tranquillity . . . however . . . you are apparently satisfied that we do mean to make an attempt to hear the word of the Lord as it is contained in the book of Hosea and you turn once more to your Bible.

" 'O Israel, return unto the Lord thy God; for thou has fallen by thine iniquity. Take with you words and return to the Lord; say unto him, "Take away all iniquity and receive us graciously and we will render the fruit of our lips . . ." Neither will we say any more to the work of our hands, "Ye are our gods: in thee the fatherless find mercy." ' "

82

It's the beauty of it I think at the back of the church among the grey heads about me. "May God add His blessing," you add, "to this reading to us of His holy word, and to His name be glory and praise." It's the beauty of the words and the voice. It's the brilliance of the imagery I explain to myself and the fragrance of forgiveness thirty centuries ago. Why have we no writing with this power these days? Maybe if we had we might consider returning to dwell beneath the shade of the evergreen cypress. But steady, Germaine steady. Here is this contagious emotion. Marvel at the beauty of the Scriptures if you like but keep your head. This is the only reason I gasp. I am part of your modern Babylon with her idolatries, whoredoms and rituals; I know I am one of your City if not the living embodiment of it but I do not cringe in remorse and shame to have a-whored from under your God. No doubt the tears I see about me belong to that category but my response is strictly my own.

Nevertheless as I discipline it and look up a dangerous tenderness suffuses. The deliciousness of sex is one thing but tenderness is another. I find myself saying to you, a man of men, seated now in the pulpit out of sight beyond the standing singing congregation, and not to God . . . *You* take away my iniquity and receive me graciously and I will render to *You* the fruit of my lips. . . .

Later on during the sermon I begin to divine at last what might be the object of your passion. I might be wrong but the way I see it at the moment it is neither God, a woman or an idea. What I see is that you could well be as madly in love

83

with your a-whoring City as Hosea with his a-whoring Gomer.

Yet I am quite unable to escape the feeling that in speaking to your City you are personally speaking to me. I don't know how I get it but I do; even from behind a pillar. And this fragrance of forgiveness turns out to be heady. It is not unlike my foreign scent except that its reach is more comprehensive; reaching beyond a mere nose to areas unsuspected. But who wants forgiveness who does not repent? I still cultivate my depravities and venerate my idols to indulge every sense I've got. People like me need reality and dare not question it. We believe in the flesh and the appetites and the senses are our miracles. It is I who am divine inside and out and I make holy whatever I do. The scent of my hair is finer than prayer and my face more wonderful than churches, Bible or any creed. If I worship one thing more than another it is my own bamboo body. I'm mad on myself I'm so luscious. On behalf of the idolatrous City I declare, "May Baal add his blessing to my statement of HIS holy word and to HIS name be glory and praise!"

Nevertheless it is at times like this, moved beyond my routine frontiers of feeling, that I become alarmed at something stirring in the fastnesses of me that must be what others call a "soul." Is this the sparkling insight you talk about necessary to the lifeless ground of science? Is this the same delirium that arises through tears to the eyes of Monsieur when he plays to me his chansons? I wouldn't want to be tainted with this; this fiery inconvenient element in some men that confuses the issue in lovemaking, spoiling the fun in play; this intangible elusive necessity that Continental critics declare to be missing in my performances; this mystical something in the make-up of the city that God values so almightily and seeks so tremendously. I have just not known what it is. All I know is that if I ever do become touched with it, it will be through the material and the mortal since with people like me the unseen must be proved by the seen.

God knows . . . or Baal knows I should say . . . I try to get away during the last hymn: it would never do to take this kind of weakness to that mortal hand of yours at the door. But three cocktails last for an hour. True I almost make it. I reach the bottom of the steps and am at the door of the Citroën before your hand catches up with mine. There was a time when I knew why men's eyes don't waver; it would be my expensive breath or my perfume speaking on my behalf or what they call my listening eyes. All of which men of men like, especially the righteous kind; the kind that professes not to. But I don't know any longer what category of man you are. You may be looking at me in this way for some reason unknown to the wicked.

"ANYWAY!" the capital letters are radiant with pulpit magnificence. "How ARE you!"

"Drunk."

Here's an exercise in forgiveness and not thirty centuries back. Your whole broad churchly figure in its black churchly gown and white collar should visibly recoil but you don't. There is no more than a firmer grip of my hand and a wider grip of the pavement, a ready-for-anything position. I am disappointed not to have appalled the Cloth it being a favorite sport of idolaters.

Round and about I am aware of a confusion of conversation; a garden of coloured hats, greetings between them who put store by greetings, who openly and actually value them, movement, interchange, an effervescence of deadly goodwill and a grand detumescence of the talking glands after an hour's continence. What had I in mind again; some rigid intention . . . yes; to defend myself from a soul. What am I doing here again now . . . this is not France . . . whose is this hand engaging mine . . .

There are trees round this church. The neon lighting of the street penetrates them hilariously sketching shadows. Talking and laughing faces and sad ones too and gesticulating

85

hands are included in them; improbable unstable and unreal they look, vibrating shimmering appearing and vanishing to the vision strongly inebriated. Your own face is unstable too, changing advancing and retreating in the busy fingering shadows and light. How can Rockets distinguish what you see from what you actually don't when the cool fresh air suddenly hits? . . . Yes defend myself from a soul . . .

The lights and the leaves and the glamour, this mirage of a congregation, your blurred figure before me . . . where is all this? In the world of the seen or the world unseen? The vibrant lights and shadows play across the inner world too so that the music within is chaotic. Diamantés sparkle on the mind as they sparkle on my gloves . . . yes defend myself from a soul. What were we talking about? I've long since forgotten. Was it the fragrance of forgiveness? The music breaks forward wilfully, the new chanson of Monsieur's called "Waiting." I look up listening wide-eyed, I don't know for how long, until I'm aware of your voice again. Anxiously I brush it away from my eyes . . . "I beg your pardon, what were you saying?"

"I was saying who are you then?"

"I haven't the slightest idea. Why, who are you?"

"I haven't the slightest idea either."

Defend myself from . . .

"Then what are you?"

"I only know sir what I'm not."

"Then what are you not?"

"I'm not one of your flock."

A long controlled silence. Then your magnificent gown-and-collar voice gives way to something more like tweeds and tie. You move with a touch of belligerency as though the Lord's forgiveness as well as your own could after all wear thin. "I trust you enjoyed saying that."

"I always enjoy what I say."

You don't answer.

86

"How are you and who are you and what?" I say.

"I'm a vanity to be offended."

"A fine answer, your own?"

"Yes . . . my own."

"I'm not sorry to have offended you. Elementary laws don't apologise."

"No."

Defend myself from you . . . "And I do not decline my wickedness."

The clerical overlay of serenity that has lifted a moment settles back in place and once more you are the controlled priest. You lift your hand and lay your fingers on my cheek a moment. "Anyway," you say to me, "bless you."

Is THIS CITY of yours as bad as the Reverend Guymer says Johnnie?"

Doctor John is resting over his wine; a very rare thing. Léon's wine I mean. He is handsome indeed. His hair waves darkly, his ears are flat, his features all in the right place and his eyes wonderful yet he's not romantic whatsoever. Especially when he takes off his wet shoes and stretches his feet to the blaze. If only you would do this. However he still has a capacity for "felicity" and his vigorous soulless technique is the most restful thing in a playmate. Let him keep his soul for his wife; it is no loss to me.

"I expect," he yawns, "I see as much of Babylon as he does." He takes some more wine. His wife and son are away for the weekend and he is not on call tonight. Me, I'm lying on the fire rug since I still can't sit after Léon smacked my bottom for being so late that I didn't arrive at all . . . that's the thing about souls in men; things happen all the time . . . on the rug I was saying and my hair comes down by accident. I'm also in the Chinese gown by accident and am scented by accident.

"Do you people really 'a-whore from under your God'? Have you 'fallen by your iniquity' and all that?"

"Maybe." A long tired sigh and a long drink of wine. "I do know there is a special squad of traffic police and plain-clothesmen being sent to this area in an effort to stop the road killings. A blitz on drinkers and speed kings."

"I was just wondering. He was so concerned about us all last Sunday."

"So I heard from my wife. But," he reflects in the flames, "we do other things between. God what lovely wine! There I am swearing falsely . . . the real Rhône this. I don't know how you get it I'm sure. I can't. In and out of our whorings we manage to build homes for the aged, homes for the young, organise societies for crippled children and the intellectually handicapped, plunket for the babies, Heritage for the care of war orphans and the Red Cross of course and my wife found herself involved only last week in taking the blind for an outing and entertaining them at home afterwards. And there's the Junior Chamber of Commerce extending young business-men in work for others . . . I can't cover everything . . . and look at the games we run at Easter, the biggest in the Southern Hemisphere, mopping up the young of Babylon and the rest of New Zealand too. And the Blossom Festival mopping up everyone else, and the Greater City Boys tying everybody and everything into one. And *then* go to church and hope we're all right. At least my wife does; the preacher is too dull for me and I'm always several jumps ahead of him. Well . . . as I was saying, there are times when I think the agnostics outside the church are doing as well as the church itself. And all from love of a kind. Charity I suppose is the word.

And all without roaring from a pulpit and accrediting it all to some Nameless Nothing. After all there's no poverty behind our Woollen Curtain, no hunger or unemployment to speak of, and no shortage of clothing. I'm in the position to see all this. It's my private opinion and my wife's too that the main body of the church is outside it and that the people might leave the church behind. The Battle of the Church will be the battle for its existence. . . . No I can't see why he should go on in the way my wife says he does; this voice of judgement every Sunday gets on her nerves."

"I wonder why he goes on like that."

"I think I know why. He believes we are not spiritual and he thinks we should be. But we seem to bumble along all right without being spiritual; as a country I mean. When you consider a few of the people we've bred I wonder what he's roaring about. Our social security has led the world, or some of it, do you know what that is? And our racial integration and our Continuous Beer-Brewing Fermentation Process, did you ever hear of that? Never mind. Have you heard of Sir Leslie Munro?"

"Who's he?"

"Chairman of the United Nations. We bred him. Have you heard of Sir Ernest Rutherford?"

"No."

"He split the atom, if you know what an atom is."

"I think I heard something like this in church once."

"We bred him too, no trouble. And other leading world personalities, like Sir Edmund Hillary, who conquered Everest, Alley of China, Katherine Mansfield of course and Frances Hodgkins and others what are their names again now . . . all bred in this little country. So that even though we are not supposed to be spiritual according to Guymer we have something else that might be as good. A pretty vital substitute. You see what's missing in your parson is . . . I've lived and trained overseas . . . what's missing in this chap is perspective. People get like that behind curtains. We New Zealanders, tucked comfortably away behind a Woollen Curtain are likely to get like that; the ones who have not travelled. We either see the very worst in ourselves or the very best in ourselves and scream to high heaven about it. We don't get a balanced outlook. Guymer is like that, seeing the very worst in us, and bombarding us with it from a pulpit.

"New Zealand is one of these still new countries with the pioneer blood still racing. I know because I see its blood in the theatre every Tuesday and Thursday when I operate. You see, my pet, even though we are not spiritual big things and big people can still happen here. . . . Apart from this biased outlook the chap's all right; probably does some good. You've got to have all kinds. Mind you sometimes I think he's mad but . . . the way he provokes the city I think is mad, against the interest of a church but . . ."

"A friend of mine says he is only a half-inch man."

"I'd be more careful about using a term like that. You've got to know a man from the underside as well as from the top before you sling round any term. I'm always seeing them from the underside . . . facing stress of different kinds. It makes me careful what terms I use about a man. The most surprising people show up well under strain. And I think I can say that I see Guymer from the underside, running into him on my rounds. And I wouldn't call him a half-inch man. Not by any means. For all that though he's not the only man who goes on rounds in Babylon, by God I can tell you that! And who wears himself out on the pain of others. I'll end up with a coronary before him."

"Have some more wine Johnnie; can you reach it?"

"I'm not saying he is not useful at a deathbed. I was just telling my wife the other day; a sure dier sat up and lived. He just sat by her bed and held her hand and prayed, for a long time. It looked all right too, quite in keeping. But if that happened too often I might have to reorganise my thinking;

91

often enough I mean to eliminate the element of chance."

I rise and refill his glass for him; it's very seldom I can get him to stay like this. "Aren't you having some too?" he says.

"Later. I want to play to you first; your tango."

"Play it now pet and then . . ." our eyes meet and make arrangements, "then I'll go over your bruises for you. Count them again," he smiles. "That was no car accident Germaine. You'll tell me the truth some day. Who the person was. Whose hands belted you like that."

I don't answer and move over to the Steinway and stand before it. But he continues talking over his shoulder. "I'm not saying that I agree with the man . . . Guymer I mean . . . he must leave a lot of bruises on minds on a Sunday; a lot of people may not be able to sit down mentally for a while . . . although there's always a place for discipline . . . but I respect him. I doubt if he's worth, as a man I mean, all the thought you give him but I always respect conviction and the courage to commit oneself publicly. Either courage or desperation in his case, I don't know which. Right or wrong he commits himself before the city." Another taste of Léon's wine. "Our paths often cross on our rounds you know. And I can't say I'm sorry to see him about. The way he handled that mother last week when that asthma I was telling you about died, just after I'd left. That child. I—I have never been too bad in a case like that but . . . but nothing I knew worked with that mother. But whatever it was he knew . . . that worked. I was only too glad to leave her to him."

My fingers rest on the foreboard in my own particular way, and still Doctor goes on talking. "I'm staking a lot, too much by miles, on his way with a young lady I've got up at hospital. I don't see any hope for her myself but . . . but I like hope to the last breath . . . and I give him all the time he wants with her. She seems to have faith in him, more than in me I think. Something goes between them that I haven't got. He told me quite candidly that he expected her to recover as long as nothing happened to upset her faith in life. She's everything to live for and knows it; husband, home, babies and . . . her youth. Youth's pretty good on faith in life."

"What's the matter with her?"

Silence.

"What's her name then? Is that the one you mentioned before? About hoping for the best and expecting the worst?"

But I can never get him to discuss his patients . . . not personally. He carries on as though I had not spoken. "No I can't honestly say I'm sorry to see him about. I've run into him in some queer places too. I met him early this week in a car, a smart Jowett-Javelin sports model, at the end of a no-exit lane. And who does this flash car belong to but a ridiculous young drunkard with a beard . . . you should have heard this boy talk! What a mess! But I left it to Guymer, I was glad to. Of course what my wife says is that a doctor should have more of the priest in him and a priest more of the doctor; her idea of a real healer, a man qualified in both. Anyway in the meantime this Guymer and I do supplement each other a little. I suppose he can take it . . . I can. I'm no religious chap but as I say as I say I don't mind him about. I like hearing him say to them 'Bless you.' "

S TEPS . . .

Steps? On a Saturday morning? Hair down, white shorts,
legs bare time? Far too much my own sober self for steps! The
iron pauses over a garment and I listen . . . hearken if you
like. But no, Germaine, it's the beat of the new chanson in
mind; I'm still hearing Monsieur's "White Furnace."

Steps . . .

But this *is* somebody! Deliberate steps firm beneath the
pondering trees. I can read sound. I know these steps mean
something. Now who could so far presume to visit me in the
morning? To no one in the whole of idol-ridden bell-clanging
Babylon do I allow a Saturday morning footing at Three
Trees, only a husband could take it. But what shall I do with
this hair . . . what can I do with my legs? Besides I'm feeling a little sick. Silence again. No one.

94

Steps . . .

Mon Dieu! It's not the traffic authorities is it! Is it time to be hauled along to the magistrate? But I hoped to meet him socially first. Footsteps at the door, the lock is turning, the door moves. No one has knocked, no one has said "May I?" Suddenly the inner chanson lurches to a halt. "How ARE you!" I hear.

Your tremendous voice strikes my studio pulverising my precious privacy. Spiders on the ceiling fall over themselves racing to their corners. Here you are standing within my doorway tall and sure and real, no longer remote in the poetic shadows of church but outrageously prosaic. I've got to get hold of my comb . . . I've got to get to my powder . . . where the devil is my poise!

"H'M?" The short syllable rattles the china and every bone in my skeleton. Dieu . . . here is the Hand! The holy open palm. Oooh . . . my poor phalanges! Hoooh . . . that's over! Whew . . . the man of God in the flesh! My organs stand up and change places.

You swing a chair into position and sit across it astride, your long legs spread each side and your long arms across the back. Is this really you sitting here mon cher? Look at your skin real and lined even pores like the rest of us and your chin dark-shaven. The hairs on the back of your hands and the nails cut and scrubbed, all earthy and mortal like other people. The texture of the black clothes, the rough surface and how they follow the line of your limbs. Do you parsons have limbs too? But isn't that too embarrassingly mortal? I can even hear your breathing. Can this be you, the Reverend Guymer, domestically a part of my Saturday morning, ironing, untidiness, nausea and all? Can you, sitting here so accessible to the senses, be that remote being I know in the pulpit who reads Hosea to us? "H'm?" you repeat innocently, "how ARE you?"

"Is this really you Mr. Guymer or are you making it up?" You smile. I must say I can take any amount of your smile

95

swinging up at the ends like this. But although you are weighing your thoughts you do not deliver them and do not answer at once. You examine the studio shamelessly from the ceiling with its excitable spiders, right round the walls and down to the floor of honest bare boards and rugs, up again, swallowing the grand piano in one comprehensive glance, the grand bed in another major glance, the open fireplace, the radiogram, the French period chair, the anemone bud in the window then home to the table with its book of chansons and find in it my open place. "You haven't told me how you are."

"I . . . survive thank you sir. In my own way." I gather up my clothes discreetly; black nylon clashes with white clerical collars.

"H'm?" you murmur reading deep in the score of "White Furnace." At the top of this manuscript in Léon's own handwriting is "To my heart." For once I am glad he has not signed his name. This is as bad as church possibly worse.

"How are you?" I try. Feeble isn't it? Why don't I pull my silly self together? Have I never entertained a man in my life? This must be the area of sentiment you preach about where science cannot guide that I'm bogged in.

"How am I, how am I," you concentrate. You stroke your mouth thinking it out then look up at me with an air of revelation. Unexpectedly you put away your pulpit voice, in your pocket I think, and your dark eyes are wide. "I manage to survive, too, curiously enough. In MY own way you know."

Isn't this conversation racing? It's about as fast as two snails in sawdust. These frightfully drawn-out preliminaries could do with cocktail treatment; a couple of Monsieur's missiles. It's true that you let me finish my sentences but I'm wondering now if this is everything. I don't think the Villain and I ever waited to inquire after each other's well-being in the euphoria of Rockets and gin and Monsieur has not asked to this day. If this snail's pace is the alternative to predatoriness in conversation then give me the predatory people.

Mind you there's plenty of time to remember to pull out the ironing cord and to think to move the kettle upon the open flame in the fireplace for coffee, that may be something . . . or do you offer the ministry wine? "You'll join me for coffee sir?"

"Oh I'm not staying," airily, "I'm not staying." You rise. "Aren't you?"

"There's an old chap here in the village I'm heading for; one of my precious old saints." But you sit down again in another position and cross all your superfluous legs. "ANY-WAY!" you continue with the weight of the world on the "anyway" as though the word accommodated all the unsaid and the unsayable banking up between us of which I sense there is much, as though it explained the inexplicable in you and divined the undivinable in me and pardoned all it divined, "it's interesting to see you in another setting. VERY INTEREST-ING INDEED."

If a sinner may be so bold it is also interesting to find you in another setting, not to mention another mood. Too, all too interesting indeed. The transition from a Sunday evening to the banality of a Saturday morning, from church to Three Trees, from holiness to commonness, from the Cloth to lin-gerie, from poetry to prose . . . now I've lost the place. Let me think . . . what did I start saying? "White Furnace" in all its hot lustful undress if only it would let me think. I brush my eyes, I try to brush it away . . . ooh yes transition. This transition from God to man is far too short for people like me. You have been easing yourself into your pastoral rounds ever since Sunday but I am caught unmasked. How like a man. It makes me conclude you are not very married to so misread a woman. You should know girls' ways on Saturday morning. You of all people should know . . . you an expert in sinners . . . should know that there is a greater distance between your towering stone church and my frank studio than a mere handful of miles; any expert in sentiment should. Even I, an idolater, know it. What part of your growing up has been skipped I wonder? Ooh but don't let me wander . . . I brush my eyes again. I find myself sitting down under the impact of all this whereas it's better to stand up for defence. In any case my bare legs are not for exhibition, not at the moment anyway. People like me who spend an inheritance on leg cream and massage don't barter the results lightly, and I've always classed my legs as a privilege rather than anyone's right and I can't see you've in any way earned it . . . not so far anyway. Ooh I could tell you of an occasion once when . . . it was once when we were making a trip across the park of Saint-Cloud to Ville d'Auray . . . but I mustn't wander; say "legs" to me another time. Where was I again? I've no idea. I sit discreetly on the pink French chair and begin modestly plaiting my hair . . . there's something aa . . . what's the word? . . . aa . . . improper? Risqué is more what I mean . . . in a whole lot of loosened hair . . . while you return to the score of "White Furnace."

There's another sentence I recall written at the bottom of that page in Monsieur Montigny's handwriting something about "Tu troubles le repos où mon âme était mise." A different selection of soul of course not the one a-whoring from God. I must take more care what sort of soul I leave lying about on a Saturday morning table in the future on account of unlikely consequences.

"You are a pianist I believe?"

"It's not I who says so sir."

"Oh?"

"I practise the pianoforte that's all."

"A musician rather. In any case some sense of purpose." You caress your mouth in this way I know. "You do not also decline a purpose."

"Me . . . purpose?" My fingers halt on my hair. "I'm neither so grim nor so earnest as to entertain any idea of purpose, sir."

"No?"

"For one thing it would bore me and for another . . . well . . . a purpose would make me unpopular."

You smile and I add, "I can't stand being mixed up in things like purpose . . . like moral rectitude and that."

The smile swings right round your face for some reason, and up and down with every little wrinkle represented. But I'm annoyed not to have appalled the Cloth. "No doubt you select a formula sir for each separate home you visit. Plainly you have none for mine."

It takes a while for the smile to come off it's so large then slowly you select not a formula but a spot on the floor between two mats and bore right down through it at something in the depths of the earth EXAMINING my remark in capital letters. Your comprehensive supply of formula I have stabbed through and through and I hear Baal applauding. *Now* where's your Master-Sentiment? You claimed it was equal to any crisis referred to it. Yet I am not exulting. That's my elusive soul down under there being examined and classified, the one a-whoring from God; the soul that neither I nor your God can catch up with nor the Continental critics. And this examination of yours turns out to be at least as gruelling as any audition I can remember, How can I relieve the poor soul? Can I lift your attention from it? "Have you a sense of purpose sir?"

You look up again with this innocent blameless look I'm coming to know also and you weigh your words in silver. "I am aware of a sense of purpose but so far only the sense. The purpose itself evades me."

I don't know what to answer because I never weigh in silver. Forgetting the exclusiveness of my legs I take up the book and move over to the grand and weigh my reply in music. It is the chanson called "White Furnace, Opus Seventy-seven, Number Three" by Léon Wolfgang Montigny which he played to me for the first time in the late dawn this very

99

morning on this very civic relic and which like my legs I classify as a privilege. The trees listen beautifully, so do the spiders but I don't know about you. And so does the anemone bud . . . but what's going on in you? As the intimacy of it deepens I'm constrained to cut it short. This souffrance humaine that so exercised my compatriote does it communicate itself to you? You do not move but that means nothing. If you do not understand music you'll never understand me which, ever since you spoke to me on the stone seat that first evening . . . but I've forgotten what I started to say. How troublesome music is this morning! Just when I'm trying to impress you.

There's so little I know about you. I know only that you're in love with your faithless city. This is the slowest I've ever been in coming to know a man . . . how much slower can I be? That's if you *are* all man. I can't share my music with anyone, not with God or anyone like that. I'd never play any of Léon's chansons to Doctor John, morning or evening, legged or unlegged. Nor with hymnbook men or magistrates. I rise and on second and third thoughts I button round me a skirt a sensational thing in C Major just made for dangerous Saturdays. I also make the coffee, the full-flowered flare opening like a garden about me as I kneel to the kettle on the hob and I change the subject and weigh my words in diamantés. "Tell me sir what brings your holy foot to this temple of Baal?"

"It's good to go where you are afraid."

"Are you afraid of *me!*"

"A bit."

"Why?"

You pause for a long time while I get out the china. I get out the white cups with the black tulips on them. "Your playing frightened me."

"Ooh that's an old story. Everyone is afraid when I play."

"You change."

100

"I have to."

Weighing again. "Yes." That's all you say.

"You don't give the impression that you're afraid when you're preaching sir."

"No?" Innocently.

"No."

"Why?"

"You growl at us. You growl at us . . . frightfully."

Smile. "Not all the time."

"Most of the time."

A wider smile. This smile of yours is one of the few not dis-jointed things about you. Couldn't you give us some of this in the pulpit? It works with people like me. But I return to my point; studying the masters all day does this to me. "All that roaring at us . . . it makes people like me think that . . . that . . . it makes me think twice about the reliability of God's love."

You look down at the same spot on the floor again weighing your words then you deliver them up peaceably. There turn out to be very few. "The love of God is constant."

"I always question anything constant." What labour keeping to the point with this inner music confusing me. It's easier driving through football traffic.

"That's lovely."

What? ooh you mean questioning anything constant. Do you think so? I don't. I pour the two coffees, my back to you. Mon Dieu I'm dull this morning! Short of a preliminary cocktail. So are you dull this morning; short of a pulpit. Indeed and indeed in this first all-sober encounter of ours, I without Rockets and you without atmosphere, I without spirits and you without Spirit we are both failing frightfully. You are as boring at close quarters as I feared. Radiant sermons and mys-tical responses plainly collide with daylight and legs. Do you know this too? You must. How could a practising minister of religion be insensitive to nuances of sentiment? You lay down

101

the incriminating chansons, ignore the prepared coffee and assemble yourself on your feet. In your authentic dignity and suspect tranquillity you take out your pulpit voice from where you put it away earlier, stroll to the door and once more deliberately set between us the old safe distance of the length of the church. "Now for my precious old saint. I haven't heard your name Miss . . . ?"

"Mrs."

The heavy eyebrows should lift but they don't. "Good morning then Mrs. . . ."

"Jones."

Your mouth doesn't drop open as Doctor John's did and you don't laugh as the Villain did. You've got on your emergency look this ready-for-anything expression that I noticed last Sunday after church. Really it is hard to shock you. "Just an unexceptional little Mrs. Jones sir." You know quite well I am lying. The three mighty trees outside stir in a lift of wind. Their solemn voices remind me of church while you finger over your obvious doubts, weigh them discreetly to yourself. But you don't deliver them this time. "All right," you decide, "Good morning, Mrs. . . . aa . . . Jones."

You have found me as I really am too suddenly altogether. It's going to be utterly impossible to attend your church again . . . without stepping up the prechurch missiles, and then what will happen to the traffic laws? Magistrates don't forgive like the Lord. I don't deliver up to you my carefully weighed thoughts either. "It was pleasant to see you sir. Come again."

Within my one doorway I see a tall man with the background of a tree beyond you, your head beautifully set forward but your face decidedly unhandsome and all your shoulders and hips and elbows and that all too clumsily set. Yet there is something . . . you've got this bearing I've noticed before only in men of the church, the physical expression of prayer. But your tranquillity still does not convince me. To people like me who study the masters up to seven hours a day conviction should come easily. Our intuitions according to Monsieur Montigny should grow as strong as our fingers and certainly as sensitive. Hours on end trying to discover what a great mind really means should leave habit in its wake but as I stand here in the C Major skirt with the silver coffeepot in my hands on this level Saturday morning the fingers of my mind won't work. I can only think you are controlling something. Your composure doesn't convince me. It could almost amount to a pose. I suspect that this admirable calm of yours is a matter of firm hands; that the ordered countenance labours to confirm what the serene white collar professes so that I find myself thinking that tweeds and a tie would suit your face more or an open working shirt and that some tussling market place blown with dust and aloud with argument would be better than the sanctity of church. As the trees rumble in the background like music within a mind I feel I'm not merely wishing a parson good morning but listening to turbulent music played by a disciplined pianist.

I move forward to go with you to the gate but how can such as I walk with such as you? How can a C Major skirt accompany a clerical collar? Even I a sinner can't do it. I stop short of you confused by the light in my eyes. But you don't look at me in the way men do. You merely stroll a step or two back to me and lift fingers to my cheek. "Anyway," you say to me, "bless you."

I can't walk all the way from the car to the church this evening so I sit on the nearest stone seat.

But it's very much nicer out here.

No doubt by respectable standards I should be in the church head down in reverence and all that but what I should be is always so boring. Anyway is this my fault? Look what you yourself did to my equilibrium yesterday morning suddenly confronting my privacy with church. My inner organs are still out of place. Where have my lungs got to and what's this up in my chest instead? It's not what I called my heart. Besides there used to be a stomach somewhere in the middle but there's something else there now. If so where's the stomach? Oh never mind where was I? I've no idea. I can only say that this pandemonium in my body is hardly what I call comfort whereas comfort is a condition I put store by. Why can't you

reverend gentlemen take more care on your pastor
What about this hazard of transition? How can a
rishioner . . . me a parishioner think of it! . . . a
parishioner switch from the man of God to the man of men
and back again all in a short weekend? To be candid I absolutely can't. Here I am trying to work my way back from
the Saturday-morning man to the Sunday-evening priest
which turns out to be such a job that I'm wearing the same
cobalt blue in G Flat as last time. What an appalling offence
to Style!

Are you trying to lose your congregation? Look at the ex-
pense of this coming to church! There was a time when it
took no more than three missiles to put me in this particular
orbit whereas tonight I've quite lost count. Moreover how
many of us can afford a perfume concentrate costing as much,
ounce for ounce, as the purest of carat gold? What makes me
come at all? I only know that I absolutely have to. This intolerable slavery of coming to church is equalled only by the
intolerable slavery of not coming. "Pray what thing can be
done worse to us than if a man should steal us away and sell
us for slaves? Now this is not done in the manner we would be
done by."

I say look at this street vibrating! Look at the buildings and
lights and traffic receding, advancing and changing places like
organs in a disturbed body. Has your celebrated earthquake
returned? What a street to build a church in and a town hall
opposite as well; a street that dances at will. What's wrong
with the foundations of this place? Is it a habit of this funny
little city to sway on Sunday evenings? Plainly there is much
about Babylon I have not yet learnt. Nevertheless it is a
glamorous place at the moment and a magic place to arrive
at. That's if I have actually arrived and all the evidence suggests I have. For one thing I've been driving for hours.

After a while . . . a precarious affable while . . . I appear to have a visitor. Now the thing about ingredients . . .

stop me if I've said this before . . . is there's no time lost in preliminaries. If I divine rightly this is the hymnbook man featuring in the borrowed-chair drama. From what I can sort out from what I can't I see a plain gentle man, maybe tall, with everything about him matching as well as vibrating; clothes and face, eyes and hair, hands and smile and dressed in tweed I think. Grey tweed of course. All of him soundly integrated and a walking Master-Sentiment. What has he come out for I wonder; to give me a hymnbook, to take up my collection or to lever me into church? Bravely he offers me a hand . . . several. "Good evening," I hear against an inner cadenza.

Which hand shall I take, this one? No this. Wrong. Try this one over here. Ah . . . got it! "Bon soir Monsieur."

"I'm glad to see you here tonight."

"Oh I *am* here then? I wondered."

"I'm perfectly certain you're here."

"Fancy! I thought I had veered off course."

"No you're here. I always know who's here and who isn't."

"Not really!" Now how can I get this hand of mine back again? It is after all *my* hand.

"I see them all from the door."

"Now isn't that interesting!"

"Most churchgoers use the door. I can count on seeing them all when I stand there. Those who go in and those who stay out. I saw you from the door when you came. You can take it from me you have definitely arrived."

"I'm delighted to have it confirmed."

The headlights of a car light us brightly then pass on. "Do you think," asks the last missile, "if I might have my hand back now? It is after all *my* hand."

"Oh sorry! Forgive me." He sits down on the stone seat too and takes refuge in the weather. "A lovely still evening."

"Do you find it still? I find things inclined to move about. For one thing the Clock Tower was no longer there when I came down the street."

"It was there when I came down."

"And for another . . . you know that railway line?"

"I've run a business beside it for the last thirteen years."

"Well that railway line . . . you do know that railway line?"

"H'm."

"Well that railway line . . . tonight it crossed the main street several times. I've never known it to do that before."

"Neither have I."

"Not that I minded," continue the drinks. "Railway lines after all have their own lives to live and if they feel they absolutely have to do a thing like crossing a main thoroughfare over and over again on a Sunday evening whereas they cross it only once during the week . . . oh I'm tired of this sentence it's too long." I cross one leg over the other. Within I hear the music; a chanson called White Furnace . . . headlights flash in my eyes again and the music withdraws to darker places . . . "But-but you see that's the kind of thing that makes me late all the time. It's not my fault at all."

"It's a good thing no train was running at the time. I'm relieved you managed to arrive."

"I'm astonished I managed to arrive. Congratulate me."

He observes me furtively in the way men do, in the way men should, but does not give up his thoughts. This is something I've got to learn in Néo-Zélandais that compliments are suspect. Admiration must be camouflaged by talk of the weather. You watch:

"These spring evenings are growing longer." There you are, didn't I say? "It's not so dark at this time now."

"So that's it. I could see there was something different about the evenings but I couldn't put my finger on what. So that's why there's more light about? The evenings are growing longer. How utterly and intricately interesting!"

"There's a new kind of feeling in the air," he says with his tongue while his eyes say more. "It must be the spring."

Or, to keep abreast with the century, the quality of the

Rocket fuel these days; if not White Furnace itself at large in the back of the mind. I know quite well without being told about this new kind of feeling in the air and that there's more light about, but why give the spring the whole credit? To people like me this new feeling and all this light are harder to explain away than as mere overtones of the spring. Not that I mean to attempt to. In no time I would be wallowing in what Monsieur calls "sanctified sensualities," music would break through and drown the issue, I would at once lose the place and forget what I set out to explain. How people like you would like to say that this new kind of feeling had something to do with coming to church and with this hymn flowing out, "In pastures green He leadeth me, the quiet waters by"; how you would like to call it joy. But I'm not romantic enough to talk about joy; I admit nothing more lofty than fun. People like me know better. This new circumstance disturbing my organs is neither an overtone of spring nor an undertone of joy. It must be something else . . . oh but this thinking is labour. Let's leave it at a new kind of feeling and if I can't put my finger on exactly what it is or on what's different about these evenings, and about these days too for that matter . . . but this sentence is too involved and I'm sure the whole thing bores me.

As ever when I try to think my infirmity catches up upon me. Here is White Furnace breaking its bounds and inundating all argument. Yet I still hear the Twenty-third Psalm. What hazards in living by music, constantly running into confusion! Two kinds of music in my head at the same time, as different from each other as these two; one from the mind of man and the other addressing God. Suddenly a third music breaks in from the jukebox down at the corner, "Kiss me hard, kiss me long!" I wake in alarm and brush my eyes. "I beg your pardon, what did you say?"

"I've just been watching you. I was wondering what you could hear."

"Nothing."

"I'm sure you were listening to something."

"I was only listening to you."

"To me . . . like that?"

"Why not?"

"No one listens to me like that, unless it's my baby girl. I'm an ordinary kind of creature and I know it."

"So am I."

"No."

"You should see me at home at practise."

"I should."

"With my hair down and no cosmetic and old slippers and you know the size of the cardigan I wear? X.O.S."

He doesn't admit his hidden words and doesn't plaster them over either. I try to see him in the complex lighting. Isn't there anything particular about him at all? Surely there's something I'm able to pin down. Has he got eyes? Yes he's got eyes. Has he got any features at all? Yes there're some features there, nose and mouth and that. Ears and so on. Even his voice, the very first thing I make sure about in you men, whether I can stand the sound of it or not at close quarters for prolonged periods, sound being my most pressing concern, in the interests of self-preservation . . . what did I start off saying? Lost. Sentence far too long. Music swirling in and out and over and under my thoughts does so confuse. After cocktails so much worse. I stare at him for a clue but all I see and hear in my inebriated vision is a dim symphony in tweed, his clothes, his eyes and his open face. He's extraordinarily ordinary. My only clue is intuition which is a mass of negatives anyway. No French rage, no ridiculous beard, no breeziness of a doctor and none of the turbulence beneath serenity found in the wake of pulpits. But what a glorious sort of man to be married to. To be so unaware. "I can't quite make you out," remark the last few drinks.

"That doesn't matter, does it?" He smiles and I do begin to make him out. Here is a sincerity not encountered in the wake of idols and I have no answer. You unlikely personalities I meet at church weighing your lives in silver. Is there any style in your lovemaking technique?

"You don't belong to these parts I believe? I haven't heard your name."

"I don't use it." The truth slips out strangely.

"You're known to us as Madame City."

"Quel nom! That's too mysterious. I've just told you I'm an ordinary girl."

"Why don't you use your name?"

"I've got one I like much better. Jones. Nothing to live up to in Mrs. Jones. No obligations, no glamour and no spurious mystery." And no reporters, no editors or photographers either. "A gloriously restful name."

"I can't follow all this. There's much that I . . ."

"It doesn't matter. It's not important."

"I prefer Madame City."

"How is a girl going to live up to a name like that? How is it going to sound in the Magistrate's Court when I hit your famous Clock Tower?"

"The Tower can take it; reinforced concrete."

"And what will the magistrate say when a Madame City smashes up his red and green lights?"

"He can take it too; reinforced concrete also." He smiles. "My name's Gordon Hood. Nothing to live up to either and sounds all right in court."

"It matches you beautifully." I look carefully at him and wonder if I can stand his voice and if he eats silently and if he understands music and a sentence from Hosea comes up, "I will betroth thee unto me in lovingkindness and in mercy," whatever that might mean.

"Come into church Mrs. Jones. I quite miss you."

"My breath too?"

"And your fragrance."

"Thank you very much; that's gallant." The old worn formula.

110

"You're welcome I'm sure; come in."

"I'm just afraid I can't."

"Why not?"

"You'll have no chair."

"You may have my chair. I can operate from a pew."

"Thank you but there're other reasons."

"Tell me."

"I've forgotten my collection."

He dips in his pocket and passes me a note.

"Thank you again Mr. Hood."

He touches my elbow, "Coming?"

"Truly I can't."

"More reasons?"

"It's too late. I might disturb the grey heads."

"They don't see you. Any more?"

"The preacher sees me. I'll disturb him."

"He has survived so far."

"I'm wearing the same suit as last time. What will the ladies say?"

"That's serious all right but they won't see you at the back."

"The real reason is Mr. Hood . . ." Can I say it? "The real reason is that I can't . . ." No I cannot say it. "It—it's very kind of you to care but I can't come in tonight. I'm quite unable to. It was such an astonishingly long way here you've no idea. I seemed to be driving for hours. I'm really quite exhausted from the effort. In the meantime I've mislaid the mood. People like me put much store by mood."

"Apparently." He releases my arm and stands before me his hands behind him in patience. "I can see," he says, "that you must have had a bad time arriving."

"Those streets were moving about."

"I'll see the City Council and have them bolted down."

"And the lights too? And the railway? Would they tie up the Clock Tower do you think?"

"I'll come and pilot you personally next time."

111

"Would you indeed? There must be more in Christianity than meets the eye."

"Few in Babylon admit that."

"Do you call this little place Babylon too?"

"It's hardly a little place now. It's a fast-growing city. We're known as the Fruit Bowl of New Zealand."

"But you can drive right through in five minutes."

"It takes the rest of us fifteen."

"But you can find your way out any time you like. You can't do that in Paris."

"We're very proud of its size."

"But you can hardly call it Babylon!"

"It has a name of its own but . . . but once the Reverend Guymer called it Babylon we don't want anything else. Or anything less. It's a name to really live up to. Or down to, some say." Pause. He clears his throat. "You said there was more in Christianity than meets the eye."

"It's all a matter of what meets the eye. Only what meets the eye." It's time I had a smoke. "On behalf of Babylon . . . we admit only what meets the eye."

"So I believe." He fingers his tie uneasily. "I'm compelled to say that it's a case of not wanting to see."

"We don't want to see what we don't like and we don't like Christianity."

"Why?"

I light up my cigarette slowly, while the cocktails do the thinking. "Because the church thinks that people like me are wicked whereas . . ." the lighter flashes, "whereas . . ." what did Monsieur say again now? ". . . whereas we are no worse than honestly instinctive."

"I must say I like that answer."

"It's the City's answer." A puff of smoke. "This dark cloud of sin makes people like me recoil against anything Christian. You know what?" Another puff of smoke. "If ever your church convinced me that I was actually as wicked as you say I'd take my pleasant life at once." I wait, while the traffic booms by and people walk past, and the hymn and the juke-box fill the street. "You should be asking me," I say at length, "why I come to church then. Why ever don't you?"

"Because I know."

"You know?"

"Oh yes I know why you come to church."

"Mon Dieu . . . I wish I did!"

"You'll know some day Mrs. . . . . aa . . ."

"Why don't you tell me now?"

"It's better to find out yourself. Just keep on making the effort of arriving . . . and I do admire your efforts . . . and it will come to you some day."

"Do tell me now."

"It will come to you some day."

I sit and listen to the inner music for a while from this picturesque stone seat between the church and the Town Hall opposite. Between a man in a pulpit on this side and another in hell on the other. But the sounds of the street in-trude in their ever ruthless way. Overlaying the drone of the traffic here is this mixture of hit tune and hymn rivalling the inner chanson; "Let sense be dumb, let flesh retire" . . . "Kiss me right, kiss me wrong!" in conflict with the inner White Furnace. In time the chanson wins: it breaks bounds like a dam, its doubled descending arpeggios growing in vol-ume and spreading out so that I no longer hear the others . . . or anything else for that matter . . . until the head-lights of a car awaken me. Now how have I arrived at this uncomfortable state? It's this unreal lighting and the trem-bling unreal street and this new kind of feeling all so confus-ing to people like me . . . I brush my eyes with energy. "I'm so sorry . . . what were you saying?" I'm divided against myself. I hear both your credo and Monsieur's. Every-thing in myself is against myself; je suis entre moi et moi. "Were you saying something?"

113

"I wasn't saying anything."

"Oh . . . so sorry."

"I've just been thinking how much I liked your answer a moment ago. About being not wicked but instinctive. I shouldn't like that answer but I do."

"Now don't you start liking my answers. I can't have the church applauding my iniquity. It would no longer *be* iniquity. With the church on my side there would be nothing left to measure iniquity *by*."

"It might be the honesty I like, or the cleanness of it, if I could only work it out. Brett would have an answer." Pause. "There's nothing new of course in finding cleanliness of sentiment outside the church."

"You're not to talk like that Mr. Hood. I couldn't stand the church approving of anything at all about me. What would Baal say? What would happen to all the fun of appalling the Cloth? What would there be left to appall? I'd stop making this effort to come. Don't mention the health of my sentiment. Baal would absolutely hate it. He's jealous of mine iniquity which he considers is of no mean order. I feel strongly about it myself."

"Christ chose his disciples from among those who felt strongly about something. He had a use for the strength of feeling."

"So has Baal for that matter."

" 'Those who choose another god multiply their sorrows.' "

"I haven't a sorrow to multiply." I throw away the butt. "In any case I don't know that I am any longer interested in this turn of the conversation."

He smiles and stands again, this time before me, his hands in his own way behind him. Not an atom of tension about this man; nothing of that unease with you about. By now he is no longer the Church Abstract but an ordinary individual man; a relationship more in my line. And it is seemly for a man to be standing before me: the exterior world reaches me

114

only through the medium of men as the interior world through music. "I am told," he says, "that you live at Three Trees."

"Three is a poor number. I prefer Two myself."

"I could remove the third tree since it offends."

"Intrudes."

"Since it intrudes. I'm making calls in that area in a fortnight. May I call?"

"I thought only the minister called."

"We help him with his visiting. Some of us . . . I've got to admit that some of us are better at visiting than he is."

"Why?"

"He's got no small talk, poor chap. People can't stand the way he will keep delving down into the lower layers or soaring miles above them. They find it embarrassing as well as unintelligible. And for his part he finds their talk too trivial. So he tells me."

"Does he?" I've got to light my own cigarette again. So far not one man in this church has lit my cigarette and not one man in New Zealand has brought me flowers. I've been meeting the wrong people in this quarter.

"His ability is in other directions."

"Is it?"

"Not that his sermons are much but they seem to have been better lately. Which brings up an interesting point. He told me this only just before church tonight. He said that he thinks someone has joined his congregation who is responsible for this improvement in his preaching. He says he feels some vital challenge that wasn't there before. Of course anyone can see there are a lot of newcomers but he can't put his finger on who."

My cigarette didn't catch and I light it again and say nothing for a change. Missiles can be too talkative.

"Some spiritual soul it must be I suppose among this new lot."

115

"Think so?" Puff . . .

"Some authentic Christian."

"What *are* his abilities Mr. Hood?"

"He's not much good at private counsel; most people say that."

"Do they?"

"They find it hard to . . . I mean he finds it hard to . . . I shouldn't say this you know."

"Say what?"

"He—he . . . he's more of a talker than a listener, he . . . and about himself I'm afraid."

"Yes but you haven't told me his abilities yet."

"I know for a fact that doctors like him about. I privately believe that . . . that his prayer is powerful. But that's not something that everyone knows. He moves about a lot of course . . . in and out of the city all the time. But—but . . . but I don't consider him a natural mixer, for all he likes to pose as one. I shouldn't use that word . . . pose. What people say is that he withdraws too much in his study reading and preparing his sermons and thinking and of course praying. People would rather have a man who was good at taking old ladies and picnic baskets with him on his rounds and who could join in a good old chat. By and large he is having a tough time here you know, Brett Guymer. The least we can do is help him with his visiting; the less serious side of it I mean."

"The less serious side of it?" I look round at him.

"It's a very big pastorate."

"What does he do the tough stuff himself?"

"He prefers the tough stuff he said."

"Mon Dieu!" I must be the tough stuff.

"Well now," he stands, "may I call?"

"I may turn out to be the tough stuff."

He laughs like anything. "I think you're the light stuff. The *de*-lightful stuff."

"Thank you so much how kind."

116

"I can do other things you know besides give out hymn-books and take up collections and . . . be kind." This is just what I've been thinking.

"Are you important Mr. Hood?"

He laughs again, but softly. "Me? I'm just a sort of a . . . no I'm not important."

"Not rich or anything like that?"

"Rich?" he laughs.

"Not too rich to chop?"

"I can chop."

"Can you dig too? You may call if you can dig and chop wood."

Smile. His teeth are his own, I see by passing headlights, and he has cleaned them righteously every morning and evening of his life. Not all straight though. "Garden trouble?"

"There is garden trouble." I tap off the ash. "Also thistle trouble, hedge trouble, trees in the way trouble, leaves and spiders-I-can't-catch trouble and there's a gate out there too with no fences to it. A selection of troubles all strictly earthy. Not the spiritual kind of troubles that would qualify me for the 'tough stuff' class. I'm the queen of the light stuff to be frank." I laugh like anything at my own joke. "Do you still mean to call Mr. Hood?"

"Have you any tools?"

"I'm just afraid my shopping doesn't run to tools." Nor my hands either.

"I'll make it Saturday afternoon fortnight. I'll bring a wheelbarrow."

"A wheelbarrow? But how fascinating!"

"And a scythe. And an axe maybe. Is your wood chopped?"

"I'm still using the odds and ends the carpenters left about. Who told you I lived alone?"

"I know. I know how everyone in the church lives . . . and how they don't."

"Mon Dieu!"

117

"And a rake I'll bring. I expect there are leaves everywhere from the winter. Now I must go in. I came out to bid you welcome."

Suddenly this rending of me again into two people; the one that lives by the material and the new one trying to emerge that shockingly talks otherwise. And this new one is talking tears. I kick her silly tears to pieces and I wish I could stand up to defend myself. "I would have welcomed you long ago but you're not all that easy to get hold of." Not all that easy . . . I couldn't stand that grammar for long. "Never being here at the beginning and never being here at the end. But," he is very cheerful about it, "I'm delighted to have met you anyway and to have spoken to you at last. As for . . . I mean, never mind about being . . . aa . . . being late. Never mind all the reasons. They'll all come right in time."

Here is the kind man I was looking for to replace Raoul. The sort it is safe to marry. No doubt he is already married and all that but . . . morality and so on, respectability and such but . . . He touches my arm. "Just keep on making the effort."

"You're kind," says the newcomer, "even human. Largely mortal in fact."

"I'll see you Saturday fortnight and I'll look forward to it. There's nothing nicer than working in the garden in spring. I love cleaning up neglected gardens." That word "love" again. Third time. How different from Monsieur's use of it and from Johnnie's abuse of it. "Good night Madame City."

"Mrs. Jones please."

"Good night Mrs. Jones."

"You won't tell anyone about the name business will you."

"You shouldn't feel the need to say that."

"No. Forgive me. Bon soir. I promise to come in next time."

He smiles again, "Good night," and turns and walks back across the pavement to the church, a physical expression of

118

the Master-Sentiment; clearly a better expression of it than you are yourself. And I wonder as I watch him walking away and hear the sound of his step whether his voice . . . whether I could stand his voice at close quarters for prolonged periods, whether he understands music, just how bad his grammar is, if he makes any sound when eating, whether he understands the making of coffee or if he is a confirmed New Zealand tea addict, whether he would take all the bedclothes with him when he heaves over at night and if he would carry me home over his shoulder from parties as Raoul always did . . . and about his technique if any.

Another hymn is under way from the church and I'm like the drunk at the door at last; demoted by myself.

But I must say it's nicer out here.

"ANYWAY! How ARE you!"

I jump frightfully; the voice is yours. Then I see two fine hands grasp the back of the seat which are anyone's but yours. They belong to the Villain in my life. "Mon Dieu! I thought it was the man of God himself. Ooh . . . my organs."

"That's what is called good theatre."

"Well don't practise on me."

"Good evening," he says in Mr. Hood's mild voice, "I'm glad to see you here tonight."

"Haven't you got a voice of your own?"

"Oh it's *my* voice you want?"

"I don't want anyone's voice just now. I'm hearing something much better."

"Maybe. But you've got to admit my entrance was effective. ANYWAY!"

119

"Don't!"

"Only the guilty jump like that."

"I'm not guilty. I've got nothing to be guilty about."

"Haven't you? Congratulations."

"No I haven't."

"Oh."

"Of course I haven't. I'm all right. What's supposed to be wrong with me anyway?"

"Go into church and find out. You might get an answer in there."

"I might get a better one out here."

"Are you not going in at all?"

A cigarette. "I'm having church outside tonight. It's cooler in every way."

"Don't tell me you're tired of being reminded of depravity."

"I'm tired of being reminded of morality."

"Are you? Others seem to quite like it. Quite a crowd went in tonight to be reminded of morality and a packed house this morning. People seem to be able to feel virtuous in the morning but not so much at night."

"I've never been able to find out the meaning of that word 'virtue,' morning, noon or night."

"You'd soon find out in there."

"I'm doing quite well out here."

Steps, steps, the sound of them passing and the humming and headlights of cars. "Would you care for a sermon from me then, my glamorous Gomer? I'm full of sermons, both reasonable and relevant and imperative to communicate. I can be acidulous, persuasive or quietly terrifying and far wittier than the Reverend Guymer. Although I must confess that my originality is apt to be masked at times by the sheer exuberance of my own eloquence."

"Don't you preach to me too; I don't feel well as it is."

But he clears his throat and his voice lifts to a purposeful major, about F major I'd say, and here he is on atheism, paragraphs and perorations of it. His words merge with the chanson on human suffering in my mind that seems to have something in common with one thing after another tonight. I turn and look up at him behind me and for the first time I really see his eyes looking into the street lights. They look like the ocean to me. As I watch them, approaching headlights illumine momentarily his whole face and I recall a painting in the Louvre. Then the car has passed and the face is in shadow . . . "Incisive don't you think?" he closes, then looks down upon me. "I say what do you think of my preaching?"

"There is no doubt about your eloquence."

A pause of pride. "My capacity for coming to grips with the intellectual fundamentals of a subject distinguishes every remark I make."

"But you look and sound as though you do believe in God, right while you're proving conclusively and brilliantly there's none."

Silence from behind me. The cold spring evening with its romantic overtones is becoming a little like church. "But it's all too deep for people like me," I add. "I haven't any long words to answer with. I say why don't you try it on the Reverend Guymer? You'd at least get replies in long words. Think of the fireworks lost when the minister doesn't hear. Do go along to the parsonage one night and preach this sermon on atheism. It would make a good story for me next time."

"Think so?"

"Do. No dressing up, no sobering up, leave on the disguise and deliver this sermon on atheism."

"I might run into all his family." He moves round from the

121

back of the seat and sits on the far end with no mean grace and crosses a long shabby leg fastidiously. "An whole lot of sticky understanding and compassion and such. Think of it."

"There is that hazard of course. But you can't waste good atheism."

A prayer and a Scripture, not to mention another record on the jukebox, later, and here is the church door opening during a hymn and my hymnbook man . . . my future husband possibly . . . looking out, no doubt checking the wandering sheep, his missing collection, making sure who is and who is not at church tonight, who might be or might not or learning some more about how we live . . . ah I've got through this sentence, yawn and all. But in the meantime the Villain has swung into another mood.

"What has a spring evening to say to me." Headlights again . . . a couple pass entwined . . . from the joint on the corner "One night with you is all I'm waiting for" . . . "I have gone dumbfounded down into the Pit. 'I have passed out of mind like one who is dead.'"

Out upon the cold spring evening rings your radiant voice that I said would reach me wherever I was. "'A new heart also will I give you; and a new spirit will I put within you; and I . . .'"

"That revolts me," he cuts in. "I tell you it nauseates me." Mr. Hood returns within and once more the door is closed. "All these gratuitous new hearts and spirits . . . it presupposes that we need them; that we are automatically sinful. That's the part that rouses me; that of course we are all sinful."

"I can't say I like that part either. This sense of sin, growing, it will drive me dumbfounded down into the Pit next.

122

And then what will Baal say? He would miss me like anything in the field. Look if that man of God in there ever convinced me that I really was as bad as he preaches . . . that I really am a very bad girl just because I . . . if ever he proves this life I live so pleasantly is after all ugly, after all my efforts to be beautiful . . . now I've forgotten what I had to say . . . damn. Anyway I'm tired of finishing sentences."

"If ever he convinced you that you were really wicked what would you do Gomer?"

"I'd take my damned life, so there." Headlights again . . . they flare then pass. "And without waiting for any of their sickly forgiveness. I'd . . . tell me, what's sinful about liking men and wine with my music, and the dawns . . . and clothes and . . . I can't see where my depravity is can you?"

"It was this same sense of sin that made me a sinner; I was inconsequent like you one time."

"Ooh change this frightful subject. Preach me some more atheism to get rid of the taste."

Another man standing before me. As he preaches out here in no man's land between God and Mammon to his congregation of one girl you are preaching inside. He preaches at least as long as you do comfortably within the church and easily as well I'd say. You should hear his pride of word. But for all his eloquence I remain untouched. Not a breath do I shorten, not a thrill record. No honey'd morphine nor mystic deliria; the temperature remains normal and the blood pressure too and the inner music waits within bounds. Nothing probes uneasy depths. Nothing wakes the wondering newcomer within me who thinks so shockingly otherwise. That's what's missing in atheism; the thrill, the poetry, the inspiration and tears and a large sensuous area is closed. I forget about the new kind of feeling in the air and my excitable organs settle. And to all this eloquent rationalism of his the crooner down at the corner supplies an admirable accompaniment. But in time my preacher pulls up with an unmistakably young sigh. "We'd better bring this sermon to a close too. Preaching, like kissing, must end sometime." Then he folds up on the seat again.

It's these entwined couples passing, their feet in step, sometimes cutting the corner beneath the church trees here to pause within the shadows that brings me to say to him, "I trust that love progresses?"

"There is no progress so far." He strokes his neck pensively. "She is never without her father and mother, except when she's in the choir and then she's next to the pulpit. If anyone wanted love to progress with her it would need to be done in full view of the congregation and beneath the eye of the minister; which would call for a technique of singular and complicated skill." He pauses while I laugh. "However," he continues, "I did hear her name this morning. I heard them call her Eliza as they passed me on the seat."

"Ooh Brother your affaire de coeur is too slow to be interesting. L'amour should be taking strides. I like to see love progress without delay to the realities."

"You're talking about common passion; I'm talking about grand passion."

"Well you shouldn't be. La grande passion could never be at home in New Zealand."

"It is already at home in me."

"Nonsense."

"It is a wound that has already begun its 'slow and magnificent irritation.' "

"Forget it, mon cher scélérat. Come up out of your Pit and see straight for a change. L'amour is no more than a sport to girls. Catch her and kiss her then move on to the next. Only touching is real. Look at those two under the trees."

124

"You are well named Gomer," he says later. "Tell me are you quite incapable of knowing anything in love beyond the physical? And could you spare me another cigarette . . . thank you. You know," he lights up reflectively, "for all your talk of realities you don't ring quite authentic yourself."

"I can't say I'm at pains to be original."

"I don't mean original, Gomer. You don't have to be original to be real. I mean you only live the top half of yourself. There must be more to you. There must be somewhere within you . . . aa . . . inner horizons that you just don't know about. Look here Gomer," he waves his cigarette impatiently, "aren't you aware of any doubts or hesitations or . . . or complicating emotions at all? How's that for a brilliant analysis?"

"Ooh forget your own brilliance for a minute. I'm not complex if that's what you mean. I'm no seething mass of magnificent irritations and . . . and inner horizons and . . . mystic deliria and all that intangible rubbish. I'm not like you and Monsieur and that boring half-inch man in there raving away at this very minute. I'm a model pattern of behavior if you must know. I'm like Doctor Johnnie. We avoid analysis and . . . and reflection and . . . and complicating emotion, anything to do with souls. He likes his operating table and I like my keyboard and that's all there is to us. I get on with Johnnie. All we can rise to is . . . all we want is to . . . to see and to hear and to . . . and—and . . ."

"And to make earthy love."

"I didn't say that."

"No you didn't actually say it. You hinted at it equivocally which is as good as saying it. When I consider what your nights must be . . ."

"Don't talk any more about me."

"Really Gomer your sensuality rises to the level of an infirmity. You put the Old Testament Gomer to shame. I wonder that you don't run out of incense to burn to the idol of sex."

Headlights, the sound of footsteps passing, the sound of delinquents round the corner, the sound of lovers' voices beneath the inquisitive eavesdropping trees. I don't know where his exuberance has gone. "I don't know that I haven't had enough of church steps and working on the wharf and sleeping in a Jowett-Javelin. I can't see in this Pit, it's too dark. If only some radiant countenance would look down upon me and lighten my darkness. Take me home with you Gomer."

"Failures bore me, when they admit it." I throw away the butt. "Anyway I can't stand this sincere conversation. What's gone wrong with you? Where has your entertainment value gone?"

"It has vanished with my gin. Melancholy pounces on me when I see life rearing up before me again in all its racking clarity. Only another drink will save me. I'm sobering that's what's wrong with me."

"I was wondering how you managed to stand. I wish I could."

"I haven't got the price of another drink on me."

"Take up this collection. It came from the hymnbook man. Look out, it's holy."

"Thank you. You know this stage don't you."

"As a matter of fact I don't. I'm not a dedicated drinker."

"You're not?"

"Of course I'm not."

"You're not a drinker? That explains everything. The porcelain skin . . . the eyes; no they didn't add up to a drinker."

"As if I'd wreck my music with drink. What do you take me for . . . a fool? As if I'd risk becoming a failure. I only drink when I'm . . . when I'm entertaining. And when I'm nerv-

126

ous. And I'm *terribly* nervous coming here. But it's the only way I can get here . . . to drink myself here."

"What do you come for then?"

"I've no idea. All I know is that I won't be coming any more. Because I'm not allowed to drink any more."

"*You* not allowed?"

"No. Monsieur won't allow me and music won't allow me and I won't. I'm beginning heavy practise tomorrow. Just wine with dinner or when a friend comes in. The maestro is training me to play his chansons. I'm going to present them in Paris myself. And you need mastery of the keyboard for work on that level. So I'm not drinking any more because I'm far more interested in sermons on technique than in sermons on my sins. I'm far more interested in the technique of music than in the technique of morality. I'm always more interested in the technique of anything than in the thing itself. In the technique of music than in the music itself. There are so many techniques in the arts; in music, in dress . . ."

"There are seventy-two techniques in the art of erotics."

"Can't you stop talking like that."

"I admit eroticism is not easy to talk about with decorum nevertheless it is the mainspring of creation. Even you . . ."

"I'd go if I could walk."

"Never mind. All this helps me to understand you a little better; your being concerned more with style than with meaning. Although when I was up there in the light concern with the meaning was considered the first virtue."

"People like me have a different kind of virtue; it is not talking about virtue at all."

Look at this street bouncing and everything and everyone in it. I brush my eyes . . . what is he saying. This way spirits have of accumulating . . . "So sorry . . . what were you saying . . ."

"I've just been wondering what brought you all this way from France."

"It was the technique of music . . . among other things. It was the maestro's reputation as a teacher that lured me to this funny little country although I wanted a break from France in any case. It's fifteen years since he exiled himself from Paris but no one has forgotten his teaching. You can forget a man's scandal but not his teaching. Now I'm his only pupil, think of it. But he's going to be disappointed you know why? He hopes I will protest at the harshness of his exercises. On the boulevards they used to say that he meant the cruelty of his methods; that he liked cruelty anyway. They used to say that's how he got results. Nothing but stark and awful exercises for years. He makes you deny music, they said, to achieve music. But I *like* exercises. I'm going to like his cruelty. I'd choose kindness in a man to live with . . . but I'd seek cruelty in a teacher. Some pianists rave about their souls. They say too much arduous practise destroys for them music itself. They say it dulls the poetic vision whatever that might mean. But not me. No poet plays up when I practise. No soul interrupts my technique. They used to say about me at the Conservatoire . . . never mind. Now whatever started me off on all this? How did I get here . . . ooh this chanson in my head . . . Anyway I'm not drinking any more like tonight. Wine and keys don't go together."

"How can this music master of yours survive with only one pupil?"

"I will have enough left after your country's income tax to keep him believe it or not. I put much store by his chansons. I've never come upon anything like them."

"It may be the spirit of New Zealand got into them."

"What is the spirit of New Zealand?"

"It is still in utero here. It only achieves birth abroad. It needs more air than can be found behind a Woollen Curtain."

"There's nothing still in utero about these chansons. It's I in utero trying to play them. He claims they have arisen from la majesté des souffrances humaines. Something I have yet to

128

learn. Ooh but everything about them's so hard. I need to be his only pupil."

"So a man of Mammon can stop you drinking where a man of God cannot. I must take time off to think that over."

"It's this man of God who makes me drink. Can't you see that? I'm so afraid of him. I've been terrified of him from the first moment I met him when he blessed me on this seat. There's so much about him and his Bless yous I can't follow . . . whole passages of him defeat me. He's an enigma and I detest enigmas. I get so agitato. I . . ."

"Fancy getting worked up over a half-inch man; a mean little half-inch man. He has a liking for attention and a flair for getting it and that's all there is to him. That's all the church is filled for these days, to see his fifth-rate theatricals. You flatter him to be afraid. He has no more natural nobility than a leather football . . . a racehorse has more."

"I think that already about him. But I'm still terribly afraid."

Suddenly he touches my glove and rises. "The last hymn . . . here come our crises."

"Don't go away, don't leave me! You must take my arm. Can you walk Brother? You've got to take my arm. I'm not well. I can't be caught by that hand!"

"Where's the Citroën?"

"Miles down . . . quick take me!"

"You'll never make it Gomer."

"Across the street then!"

"Across the street? What good will . . ."

"Monsieur."

"Come on then get up."

"Monsieur can have the end of this story. Take me across the street from the Reverend Guymer to Léon Montigny. From God to Mammon . . . from sanctity to sin."

"Get up, you're not trying."

129

"I am. Come on stir in the next ingredient, the fourth man, and end this involved lesson."

"Never mind the talk, try walking. Put one foot in front of the other."

"Which one?"

"Either will do for a start."

"My cocktails have accumulated . . . what'll I do."

"Bring up the other foot . . . that's what you'll do. Take it further can't you? Put it in front of this one. Now take your weight on it . . . oh your fragrance! Now bring up the rear foot. Excellent. Your perfume . . . I'll never forget this moment. Now the foot behind, bring that along. You forget a girl's face but you don't forget her perfume . . . the doors opening. Can't you do it more quickly girl?"

"Is that the benediction?"

"Stop while this car passes."

"I can hear the benediction."

"Wait, careful . . . a truck."

"I still preferred your sermon though. I still value every note of my depravity. Are we going to stand here all night? What'll the Reverend say?"

"You are soft to touch . . . Gomer . . ."

"Don't let him catch me! I can run . . . watch!"

"*Stop!*"

Cry of brakes . . . someone shouts . . .

"Don't let go like that! Hang on to me! Now then . . . forward. Keep straight."

"I am straight. It's the street that's moving."

"Hang on to me I said!"

"I'm . . . sick . . ."

" 'The Lord bless thee and keep thee.' " Your radiant compassionate voice. " 'The Lord make his face to shine upon thee and be gracious unto thee. The Lord lift up his countenance upon thee,

and give thee peace.' "

130

A COLD Sunday evening . . .

You wouldn't think would you? that I could hear a discreet knock on my one door with the left hand running in the bass as it is but I can quite easily. I can hear just about anything you know long before other people which is a quality of my infirmity. I can hear birds breathing a mile off or at the height of a New Zealand storm. So I leave the keyboard where I have been working in cool sobriety and stroll towards the door; slowly . . . giving myself time to sort out who it is, who it . . . look at the small white petal lying alone on the dark table from the flowering Prunus I put out this morning, a still petal, just one, with no branch, bush or background . . . giving myself time to . . . but I doubt if I'm in the mood for anyone whoever it is. This nausea that is not quite nausea I've had for some weeks and this unlikely loss of interest in men. Even people like me have their worries. Consequences can rise to the level of crises at times have you found that? Or can you manage to avoid these consequences? Gastric flu Johnnie said; strontium 90 in the blood is what I say. Where was I now . . .

Theoretically it is my lyrical compatriote in exile Léon Montigny but when did he ever come on time? Is Johnnie out this way on a case? If so he likes this gown. I know all right where *you* are . . . in a pulpit of course at this time, about as far as the second hymn. It won't be my eloquent Villain; he'll be keeping his impassioned vigil at the church door. Whom else do I know who might be drawn to visit me on a Sunday evening . . . not the traffic cops surely! I smooth the embroidery on the Chinese gown sweeping softly to my feet, touch my hair, sniff briefly and privately then turn the old-fashioned door handle. Mon Dieu! The blast of the night!

The hymnbook man! I had quite forgotten him. Of course, he promised to come and pilot me personally to church! I never thought about it again. But he's that sort of man; the kind who says things you never remember. Not that I mind seeing him here in all his self-effacement but what about Léon due to arrive any time? I'm not in my blue gown for nothing with its buttoning from throat to toe. Why don't you men ring before you come? What a lot you men of the church don't know about the technique of playing. "Mon Dieu!" I breathe.

"Good evening! I'm so glad to find you safe."

"You should be at church."

"I was. But you didn't arrive. I was concerned for your safety. I thought you might be having trouble with the railway line again . . . and the Clock Tower. I began to worry when you didn't come so . . . I remembered my promise to come and pilot you."

"Did you think the magistrate had caught me?"

Smiles.

132

"Did you think I was at court instead of church?"

"I didn't know what to think. I had to come and find out. I pictured you wrapped round a red light. I'm most relieved to find you safe."

"Oh . . ." The rain is wheeling round in circles, running like a left hand all ways and my gown is not built for it. Neither am I for that matter. But how can I ask him in? Would you ask in a gentle lamb of God with a raving lion in the offing . . . a raving Léon I mean? It is hardly good technique. Not that crises of this kind are unfamiliar to people like me; there are all sorts of ways out.

"Perhaps," he tries not to glance the blue length of me, "you did not intend to set out anyway . . . the bad night?"

"No . . . I didn't."

"Well never mind." He holds on to his hat. "As long as you are safe. I've had some bad moments."

"Oh . . ." I'm overdoing this ohing. "Thank you for having . . . for having bad moments on . . . on my account, Mr. Hood. That's . . . that's so . . . so Christian of you."

"Not so very Christian. Not wholly I mean." I know all about this dropping of a man's voice to a whisper and all it recounts and foretells. Does he know how much he reveals? But I want it to drop this way particularly with Gordon Hood. Yet all this still won't do. I've ideas about this kind man and running into Léon Montigny at my studio on a Sunday night is not one of them.

"Do you think I can persuade you to come to church after all? You can have my chair." He grasps the door high above me and leans over. His coat is fairly stylish, well-cut with a belt; grey of course. And a pale pastel scarf neatly tied. And his hat is spruce; grey again. Orderly he is, everything about him right and nice you know what I mean? Gloves and that, leather. I myself have difficulty in not dwelling on the length of him I like men leaning over me, it gives me that sort of feeling . . . you know? The feeling that he's first with me. The man with me at the moment is always first with me . . . for the moment. This kind of moment is . . . never mind. Say moment to me later . . . Softly, "I'll take you there in my car and bring you home. I'd like to."

"Would you?"

"It would be a privilege."

"Thank you so much."

"Unless you wish to get on with your music."

"No."

"I'd like to take you home after church to my wife. For supper. She'd like to meet you."

"Doesn't she come to church too?"

"We've got three babies." A short laugh. "I'm a bit old aren't I to be talking of three babies. I married late, a young wife."

"Oh . . ."

"We can get people to baby-sit of course but . . . but she hasn't been well lately. She's just home for a spell . . . from hospital."

"Oh. Thank you but I'll come home. I often get back to practise after church."

"Mrs. Hood could get you into the life of the church if you got to know her. This living alone must be hard on a girl. I'm sure she'd like to do that. She doesn't get out much with the little ones and she . . . it's something for her to do to take an interest in a newcomer. She . . ."

"Actually I'm expecting a . . . I'm expecting to have a lesson after church. I'll have to . . ."

"You'd rather come straight home, right."

"What, I am coming do you think?"

"I think so."

"I'm anything but strong on decisions."

Smiles. "You're coming."

"I'm not dressed; not for church." A dull rumble in the storm; is it Léon's low gear! Stuck in the ditch?

"I'll wait for you to change." No the roar in the trees it is.

"So I'm coming?" Crisis nearly over. "I won't be long. I can't ask you in Mr. Hood . . . not while I change. I've only got one room." Wouldn't Johnnie laugh at that! So would Léon. What would you do . . . laugh too? Or turn on your emergency look? But I've ideas about this Gordon Hood as I've already said and undressing before him at this stage is not one of them. Not yet anyway. It's anything but good technique when you mean to marry a man, babies, sick wife and all. "Would you mind waiting out here? It's cold I know but . . . it's wet too but . . ."

"I'm only too pleased. I'm sure you won't be long."

"I won't be long. I want to be in time for the Reading."

Zooming along in his big car through the dark orchards with the rain smacking the windows . . . what a big car! it must have hinges in the chassis to get round these corners and rows and rows of wheels; a sort of upholstered centipede. Sumptuous . . . he must be rich. What I'm short of is some source of information about people I meet at church; some luscious gossip who knows all the detail. You men so far are all just sketches with no filling in or background; as I am to you no doubt. We live with each other only in conversation and in short flashes of nearness.

His eyes are on the watery road but I know the Strontium Ninety must have reached him. I can tell by his short abrupt sentences . . . "You didn't set out at all then?" and by the way he doesn't mention it.

"No I didn't I . . ."

The undersong of the engine and the Strontium . . . I carry on, "I . . . you see . . . coming to church I always have to d—I find it too hard to say what I . . ."

135

"I think I know what you mean."

I cross one leg over the other. A knee emerging from fur has its value. It looks pathetically slim. This knee is under the black-and-white lightning suit; a suit that can take over it only a coat like the squirrel. "You do know what I mean? I wish you did."

"I'm perfectly certain I do."

"I was really not coming to church any more it's . . . too difficult."

"So I see."

"I've started work this week with my music master and he's strict on training."

"It's lovely to hear it. I was waiting quite a while outside your door you know. I couldn't bring myself to interrupt you. That left hand running . . . galloping. I've never heard such brilliance. The whole setup . . . forgive me if I'm bold . . . it's too astounding. Music of that . . . that frightening quality coming from a whare * like that. The left hand . . ."

I smile. "Monsieur says it is a lazy hand. Reluctant. He calls it the reluctant hand. Look here's the Clock Tower, quite still. And the railway line not moving. Funny that . . ."

"They know better when I'm about."

"It's nicer with you about."

"I'd like to think so."

Pause . . . for a block. "You may think so."

Several blocks along the main thoroughfare in silence and he slows at the church corner. "I'm dying to say something if I may."

No answer.

"I thought you would be like this when you were . . . untroubled."

"Like what Mr. Hood?"

"May I say it?"

* WHARE—*Maori for house.*

136

"It all depends."

"I thought that when you were . . . untroubled . . . you'd be as beautiful in yourself as your . . . face."

He draws up into his original place at the kerb directly below the church steps. "Thank you . . . Gordon."

Another conversation closing with nothing supporting it; no background behind it; no knowledge of the man himself. A petal dropped on the waters from some bush upstream so far unknown to me. That's how I see these recurring brief interchanges with you men of the church I meet; petals floating by on unfathomed waters. Do you see it like that? Or can you visualise the bushes they have fallen from? Can you divine the essence of a man after a few slight words? I can't. I need more than a few slight words. I understand little more than what I see and hear. All you men I've met lately . . . what is the essence of you? What is the composition of your lives? What keys are they written in? What soil have you arisen from . . . your homes and families and work and ways? All that comes to me is the face value of what you offer me; I can only stab at what you mean and are. So that this short flash of talk with Gordon Hood is once more no more than a petal floating.

Here he is already leaving my side as we enter the church . . . very late indeed . . . and sitting ahead of me in a pew. Why not sit with me? Because of what people might say? Something I am finding hard to learn in this country; this furtiveness between men and women. Might Mrs. Doctor John tell it back to Gordon's wife at the next church social? Might Mr. and Mrs. Dalgliesh, Eliza's parents, broadcast it the length of their three-thousand-pound drawing room? Because your wife, whoever and wherever she is might see

137

him? Strange thing this insular morality. How can anyone acquainted with la Vénus noire with her ebony thighs and the hell of her bed see sin in sitting with a man in church? I'll never learn it. What would I ever achieve, least of all another husband, if I let talk qualify what I do? Not that I'm unpractised in discretion, it's one of my twenty-three personal commandments but never mind what was I thinking? Yes . . . it's over, this brief converse with the first man this evening. Until the next time; until Saturday afternoon to be accurate with its talk of rakes and wheelbarrows . . . if that can be reconciled with ebony thighs. For you don't think I'm letting Gordon Hood drive me home after church do you, with Léon waiting there? Moreover I don't take so lightly this not sitting with me business. A little discipline hurt no man. ANYWAY . . . over is the brief interchange; passed by the floating petal.

And now your turn, mon cher. Number two for the evening. More interchange with no knowledge of your life. Another petal of converse floating by on the dark waters of mystery.

I find when I have brought my attention out to you that you have already begun. I find you speaking with a calm that may fool others but not me; at least I have learnt that about you. And I discover that you are quite disconcertingly easy to follow when I'm free from the fire of ferment.

"There are some of us in this church," you are saying, looking over our heads with that assumed innocence I know, "with intentions other than godly. It may amuse us," your voice is deceptively soft as you glance at the notes before you, "to hear them enumerated.

"Some of us come," you set out . . . We do hear these intentions enumerated; all boring and well known until after a while your voice lifts: "Some . . ." and here we are approaching a point of considerable interest to me . . . "some, afraid of the magnitude of our depravity and anxious to get on side with God at least once during the week, come running into this house called by His name to declare to ourselves 'This is the temple of the Lord, the temple of the Lord, the temple of the Lord.' " You pause and lift a page . . . I'm still in the dark why I come. "But," you continue, "very few to serve God. I prefer the loiterer on the steps myself; at least he is honest in his atheism." You glance casually round the full congregation then concentrate on a large bowl of spring flowers nearby as though vastly preferring them also.

After all of which we hear that you intend to set exams on the Prophets you have read and on your obsessing Master-Sentiment, to check up on us all, your voice at times shooting to the roof like a steam bore and at other times, dying, controlled; still addressing the flowers rather than us. "I am weary," you confide to them, "of preparing sermons for apparently nothing and I'm moved to do something about it. There is a proverb I have in mind" . . . do you glance at me? " 'Speak not in the hearing of a fool, for he will despise the wisdom of your words.' " You pocket your hands somewhere beneath the academic gown, move a little in the pulpit then mildly announce the next hymn.

"Hear the word of the Lord as it is contained in the book of Jeremiah; chapter seven, verse one . . ." Some people are marking it in their Bibles. What a good thing I am not in orbit. I would not have known I was called a fool. Church is quite different when I'm sober; I can hear what is said about me and can keep both hands on reality.

" 'The word,' " you read innocently enough from the great book before you, " 'that came to Jeremiah from the Lord: Thus saith the Lord:

" ' "Amend your ways and your doings and I will let you

dwell in this place. Do not trust in these deceptive words, This is the temple of the Lord, the temple of the Lord, the temple of the Lord . . ." ' " A chapter of sensuous and powerful language about the wrath of God poured out upon us until you arrive at your ending we know so well, "May God add His blessing to this reading to us of His word. . . ."

By the time the anthem is over however and sermon time has come my laboured concentration has worn thin. As you lean forward to observe us with nothing left now of the look of childish innocence I lose the place again. As your voice begins in threatening softness I fall to speculating in my old way on your background. What is behind and beneath these brief meetings with you from the back of the church to the front? What is the nature of the bush upstream that has cast tonight's sermon? I know you are made of flesh and blood, I found that out when you called on me, but do you live a flesh-and-blood life? What sort of home is the Parsonage? What kind of wife do you use? Have you any children or are you too moral to beget? What do you do in the evenings? What is your past, have you got one? Or are you priests too holy for pasts, just beings like angels, appearing and disappearing? From the look of you, unhandsome, unspectacular and unattractive, I would suppose an highly casual origin; you would not bathe overmuch and would probably eat noisily. Tell me, what do you know of love, anything? Have you any grand passion other than that for your City? And how close do you get to your City, this young giantess conceiving each day her gargantuan children; do you "sleep in the shadow of her breasts"? How skilled is your technique if any? And tell me, for how long is this Sunday hour to remain no more than a flash of nearness, a passing petal on the deep waters of the week? For how long is . . . Mon Dieu, what is happening to your sermon! What have you been teaching; what about the exam! I brush away the wilful images and

140

reassemble myself. Still travailling you are, still ploughing away through your subject, turning another page, your voice having a wonderful time.

"We read that His anger will be poured on this place. Living in this century of nuclear fission we are all too well acquainted with what kind of anger. Think, my people of Babylon: what manner of anger could burn without quenching, both man and beast, the trees of the field and the fruit of the ground the whole world over? Are we ever . . . EVER!" . . . boom . . . boom . . . boom! ". . . ever going to listen out of our own wisdom to the word of God or must He speak eternally in the hearing of fools! Are we going to continue ignoring Him until forced to listen in the extremity of fear? And will it be of any avail then . . . THEN! . . . to rush into this house called by God's name to babble 'We are delivered! This is the temple of the Lord, the temple of the Lord, the temple of the Lord?' " In silence you hold us, then . . . soft . . . "Think that over, my people."

"I need two things," I tell the Villain as we shelter together in the portal both from the rain and the last hymn . . . the diamantéd rain spangling down the street-length in the muted neon lights. Here is the third man in sequence for the evening and, as both you and Gordon Hood were, first in importance for the moment. Another flash of converse coming with no backdrop support whatever. What is the secret of these black waters? Can it be possible that he actually has a history and even a name? How does he come to know so much theology? I would have picked him as an actor wouldn't you? What has brought this eloquence of his to the bottom of a pit and his magnificent irritations to these steps? What is the nature of the bush upstream that has cast this roaming petal? My own roots have not yet struck deeply enough in this country for me to anticipate these things. In Paris it would have been no trouble to . . . or is it because you are men of the church? So spasmodic, superficial my engagements with you men near the church still no more than just one conversation after the other. Where are the action and the realities of Doctor and Monsieur? My own roots have not struck deeply enough in this church I mean, as well as in this country. It makes me wonder if I've arrived at all or anywhere for that matter. This hazard of unfamiliar thinking whenever I come near this place, this sense of some unknown area within me opening that is hardly a quality of people like me. Have I been careless enough to have drifted into the very area of sentiment you have so often preached about? Am I after all someone else? Out in the fairy-tale rain reality seems poised in suspension . . . but this confusing inner music . . . where was I? I brush my eyes earnestly. "I beg your pardon. What were you saying? Sorry I . . ."

"I was just asking you what two things you need."

"Two things?"

"Now don't slip me up in the middle of a story like that . . . It would be called mental cruelty in court. What . . . ?"

"Ooh yes . . . a taxi the first is and the second is . . ."

"A taxi? What about the man who brought you?"

"I can't have Gordon Hood driving me home I . . . I can't have a hymnbook man throwing himself into the works at Three Trees not tonight anyway. Not with a green suit sitting at my keyboard this very minute with the chansons before him and the Rhône wine beside him. I can't have . . . it would not be good technique. I . . ."

"You're not going to give Mr. Hood the slip are you? For a minor reason like that? Don't be so immaturely amateur. You French are known to be better qualified. Walk right in on Monsieur the two of you and announce the next hymn. Think of the theatre of it!"

"It would be too much of a strain on my technique."

"It wouldn't be on *my* technique. Take me along too. I'd be wonderful audience value."

"Two's enough without three . . . Mon Dieu!"

"Are you confessing you can't take your men in twos and threes?"

"I take my men in ones; it's the foremost quality of my technique. I've got to be simple with myself you know I've got no subtlety. That's one of the virtues of people like me . . . simplicity. Men in ones . . . toujours. Doesn't matter how many the grand total but they've at least got to arrive in ones. It's another of my twenty-three private commandments I use in place of the famous Ten; always keep your men apart. If there's anything I can't stand in the art of playmating it's . . . all of which reminds me of the second thing I need. I need a drink by God!"

"You'd all need a drink I should say after what you got in there tonight. I don't know how you congregation can take such aggression, such humiliation such intimidation. I'm inclined to the view you all like it otherwise how can you possibly stand it?"

"That's just it I can't. It's very bad for my sense of sin. This idea of sin is so new to people like me. It's like a great big black Almighty Avenger hovering over me." I cover a yawn, not a Rocket yawn but a night-before one only. "Did you hear the names he called us in there tonight? Or don't you hear the deadly soft places out here?"

"I liked the part about the plain and fancy adulterers. Tell me Gomer do you fancy the plain or the . . ."

"Ooh you do jump to conclusions! I'm much more circumspect than you think. You don't know what Léon said; he said the woman in me was still virgin."

He thinks a moment earnestly. "A strain on the word 'virgin' I feel."

"Stop it. Did you hear him say 'Do not speak in the hearing of a fool?' I say where does that come in the Bible? We might get a question on that in the exam."

"Don't tell me you're . . . whacko! But Gomer. People like you couldn't pass exams like that. Master-Sentiments and such. And what do you know about the prophets? There won't be any questions on Style you know; and on the frivolities of fashion. There'll be nothing on the qualities of Strontium Ninety as a Master-Scent or on the radioactive line. Number three question is not likely to be on the most effective ingredients of a Rocket cocktail, or number four on the technique of love-making." He laughs with irrepressible gusto. "You won't find number five asking what happens to the soul when kissing has to stop. No, my inconsequent sinner, you'll just have to stand it and like it."

"I'll be called a fool by no man."

"Gomer roused at last! Don't tell me you've got feeling below that surface. Gomer training for the Battle of the Church in this century . . . hurray, hurroo! Forward the Church Brigade! Onward Christian Soldiers! Noble Six Hundred!"

"Oh stop it! All I'm likely to do is to show him that we in this city are not all the pack of morons he appears to believe we are. I'm not Madame City for nothing. I have my responsibilities to Baal and I mean to honour them. I'll show him whether or not he is speaking in the hearing of a fool . . . I say where *does* that come in the Bible?"

"It's a proverb of course. Chapter twenty-three, verse nine."

"How do you know these things?"

"You don't have to know much to pass anything he sets. Do I have to sit his piffling exam to prove it?"

"You'd fail. You'd fail from the sheerest habit. You'd try to fail, you love it. You're all talk and no wisdom. You don't weigh your words in anything."

"Don't I? I belong to the twentieth century remember and not thirty hundred-odd years back. And when I need wisdom there is always the pub on the port. Down there we weigh our words in something far more expensive than silver; we weigh them in fuming gin."

"If only he could hear that. I say do sit his exam too and write him some of those answers. I'd feel better if you did."

He waves a picturesquely ragged hand. "I could pass that exam with both hands tied behind my back and both eyes blindfold. And it would bring him down a bit to have to realise there was knowledge of the Bible outside the house called by God's name; at least as much as he would find within it. In the pub and on the wharf and in this joint at the corner and even here on the steps. An exam from him would be chicken feed."

"I'm not so sure about that. I've missed a lot so far. Well I've got to find a taxi and a drink. A taxi to get away from this centre of censure and a drink to get over it all. You've no idea how this sin business is beginning to worry me. I must get home and fast."

He pulls what he calls his coat about him and fingers the token buttons. One is a large pearl clasp and what's this . . . a paper clip? "Some day I might find you down in this Pit with me. Company. If you continue to take sin so seriously. Now I've got to go and sit on that seat."

"Don't be silly! You can't sit there in the rain. Go and stand in the porch at the choir entrance."

"It's too public and lit up in there. Besides I couldn't be so obvious. Is that water on that seat can you see?"

"L'amour won't progress sitting in a pool of water."

"It's got to be that seat. That's exactly where she passes each time."

"C'est bien." I fasten the hook of the squirrel coat at my throat and pull up the cowl at the back. "Go and drown yourself if you must but from my reading of la grande passion it's a bit early in the opera to drown yourself. That's what they do when the kissing stops, not before it starts. I'd be a little more realistic myself if ever it came to me. Now where are these taxis?"

Down the first step again. "Just round the corner?" Down

145

the second step and stop in the rain. I'm never good at leaving youth for middle age and always make a lot of false starts. I find it so hard not to marry youth but they're only good for love-making and nothing else. It takes middle age to feature comfort. Make sure of the comfort I say and find the play where you can. . . . "What did you say? Sorry . . ."

"You're always going," he complains.

"I've got to. There are two men now who might catch me if I linger too long. Now where are these . . ."

"Two blocks up the main street then turn to the right. You should have an umbrella or a hat like mine."

"I like the rain on my hair." Our voices are muted in the rain, as the voices of the hymn are too. Rain is a wonderful muter; it's kind. It softens hard sounds and you don't feel the edges.

Here is another conversation closing; another flash of near-ness with nothing before or after, or underneath for that matter. Another petal floating by on the dark waters. My whole sojourn in this country . . . stop me if I've said this before . . . has been little more than a single petal drifting on unfathomed waters. True I draw sustenance from Mon-sieur but he's a compatriote. Another reluctant step down. "I love the sound of the rain," I say. "The way it mutes all other sounds . . . integrates everything. Like his boring Master-Sentiment." It's a kind of Master-Sound in which even the hymn and the jukebox merge. I wish I had some Master-Experience to integrate all others. I picture some-thing happening to me that joins me up closely with every-one else; something that assembles all the passing petals into one full blossom and shows it growing on its bush. . . .

"You shouldn't be taking those wistful eyes into the street at night little Gomer. They'll get you into trouble. You should never risk walking alone at night at all. Babylon can be dan-gerous. Can't you cover up more of that face somehow? It's too much of a temptation to men."

I glance back at him with suspicion. "I get the feeling sometimes you are kind."

"Pure accident. Inadvertent. A bad habit I've caught in the past."

I examine him a little longer then proceed to the bottom of the step.

The rain is on my face. Suddenly I turn and hurry up again and look closely beneath the brim. Two dark oceans for eyes I find. I whisper urgently: "Do you know what he's setting those exams for Brother? To cast me out of his sight. He actually read the words: 'I will cast you out of my sight!' And he glanced at me as he read them." I touch the shabby sleeve. "I don't think he likes this influx to church do you? Did you hear him say he preferred you loitering at the door? I don't think he likes me in church. I think he means to frighten me out. I think he just likes that handful of grey hair at the back as it was when I first came." Muted headlights claw through the rain-spangles and light us momentarily. They claw onward and we are darkened again. I lean closer. "Gordon Hood told me that the Reverend told him that he felt a difference in the church lately. He told Gordon," I whisper with an air of scandal and revelation, "about some unidentified newcomer who he sensed was challenging him. You can laugh but . . . don't you repeat this will you? . . . but I thought it might be I. But now . . ." I pocket my hands and straighten, "tonight I know better. I know now he doesn't want me. He doesn't want me here at all." The sparkling descending rain-curtain, street length, with its millions of diamantés and spangles. "It must be someone else stimulating him. It was I he was thinking of when he quoted about speaking in the hearing of a fool. *I* know! I've always made such a fool of myself whenever I've met him. But you see . . . you see Brother! . . ." I grasp his long wet hand, "it's because I've always been so afraid of him! I've always just been drinking! Because he makes me drink from

147

fright that's why! Only tonight I didn't drink but that's because Gordon brought me." Back down the steps a little into the muting rain again. "Nice preachers shouldn't frighten girls. They shouldn't call us fools. It's not done among people like me. In my own habitat I'm received with the greatest respect. In the cafés on the Left Bank and at the Conservatoire and in the concert halls and on the boulevards . . . even Monsieur has respect for my name." Another step down . . . into the softened sounds of the street. "I won't come to this place again . . . and this time I mean it. He can attack my morals but not insult my intelligence. Besides," I look through the rain to the corner joint wistfully, "I get such a feeling of my own evil in church. That's the main thing about it I can't stand . . . now a taxi, I must go. It's too much of a hazard talking here." Home to the studio, the temple of Baal, and to the fourth man of the evening whom they said in Paris killed a whole live woman with a knife and who hasn't a flicker of shame and all she said to provoke him was "Don't touch me Léon." That's all think of it! It must be something he really dislikes. "Au revoir Villain. May l'amour progress."

He follows me down the steps and a hand alights on my fur. "Gomer," the rain drips from the hat brim, "there's no time to answer you; this is my awful crisis. Any time now in the next ten minutes I may touch the coat of Eliza Dalgliesh. Do you realise that this hymn drifting out contains her physical voice? The thought alone almost heals me. I feel the Pit less dark. Tonight, soon, I may touch the hem of her garment and she will never know, as Christ did, that her purity has made me whole."

"The way you believe in this thing! The power of healing in a touch. You're a rattling good positive thinker. It could well come true, from my reading of it . . . there's that benediction! I must not hear it! Let me go Brother! Au revoir. May l'amour pro—"

148

"I hope you have let Mr. Hood know you are vanishing like this."

"No I have not."

"He won't know what's happened to you."

"He should have sat with me in church."

"Don't hold that against him. Custom is very powerful in this country. Leave a message with me. He'll be beside himself."

"Oh he'll survive . . . they all do."

"You don't bother too much about courtesies do you?"

"This is the Parisian brand."

"You could do with a year among savages to learn manners. Among cannibals, to be accurate."

"You're mad. What have manners to do with playmating?"

"Good manners have their source in kindness."

"You don't know men as I do. They thrive on being slipped up."

"All right then. Good night . . . good night. But can't you hide that face? I'm so . . ."

"What's that?" I look up listening. I pause in the rain descending and swinging like a theatre curtain. Oh . . . only the new chanson, "May the night bear my breath away." It sounds as though it were outer music. Listening to it I still feel the rain on my exposed neck underneath my chin and underneath my mind I feel the charge of this new feeling in the air . . . "Sorry what were you . . ." I brush both the rain and the music from my eyes. "Hell isn't it wet out here! I must . . ."

"You look so little in the rain . . . the first time I've seen you look . . . well, lost I suppose is the word."

"I haven't really struck roots in this country, not deep enough anyway. Nothing is joined up together as the rain joins everything together: into one acceptable symphony. I haven't got words to say what I mean. I thought I'd struck a root when I first came when he took my hand one night,

149

the first night after church; hard and firmly he took it and held on to it. I felt then I had touched something. I suddenly felt I . . . well, struck a root I suppose. But now that I see he doesn't want me, and I think he doesn't want me here, I no longer feel that way. I haven't struck a root at all. Struck anything for that matter. You can laugh but . . . what I feel is . . . is that I'm something not attached. Something with no . . . no sources to draw on. I—I'm just like a petal floating . . . passing by on waters unfathomed . . ."

From here of course I should go on to talk to you about the fourth man for the evening, Monsieur, and tell you how he ripped off my clothes and tore them to pieces and thrashed me for saying a harmless little thing like "Don't touch me, Léon." And how, deep into the dawn, I rang the fifth man:

"May I speak to Doctor John."

"Who's speaking please?" A woman's voice, clipped, efficient.

"Mrs. Jones from Three Trees."

"Oh. Doctor is asleep. He's very tired. Is it urgent Mrs. Jones? Doctor is not on call tonight you know. There are two doctors on duty at the hospital. The number is . . ."

"I want to speak to the doctor please."

A silence at the end of the line . . . a wait . . . "Hullo?"

"Come to me Johnnie."

"What's the matter?"

"I had an accident."

"What . . . again?"

"The car."

"How bad are you?"

"I'm . . . I'm bruised."

"Any punctured skin, any bleeding . . . broken bones?"

"No just some funny pains in my back coming and going all the time."

"Hang on then, I'll be there. Keep warm, lie still."

Let me off the fourth and fifth man for the evening.

"I feel drowsy Johnnie."

"I should damned well think so; you've had a hundred milligrams of pethidine."

"What's that?"

"A derivative of morphine."

"Ooh yes, that's right. What happened?"

"Look on the table, in the water."

"There's nothing there . . ."

"In the wineglass. It's all I could find handy at the time."

"What's that in the wineglass?"

"The baby."

"I don't know what you mean."

"Now lie down. I've had enough from you. Lie down I said!"

"But I don't know what you mean! What's . . .?"

"I mean . . . that's our baby."

"Our . . . do you mean I've had a . . . a baby . . . a *baby!*"

A long sigh and no reply. He is stretched out in the old pink chair.

"But I didn't know I . . . !"

"You made enough fuss about it."

"Give it to me . . . let me see!"

"No."

"Give it to me . . . I want to see it! Oooh! But where's its hands and feet? Is that blob its head? I thought they . . .

151

it's not complete is it. I thought they'd be babies at once. It looks more like a . . . a wounded shrimp or a . . . what d'you call those things . . . a tadpole. No Mon Dieu! Y'know what it looks like? An embryo Baal. No longer than my nail."

"No."

"Did *I* make a thing like that? Well I think I'm wonderful! That's the cleverest thing I've ever . . . well cheer up! Aren't you glad we've had a . . ."

"That's my daughter. I've always wanted a daughter. I'd have been a better man had I had a daughter. I've seen other men with their daughters, the way they rave about them. She might have been beautiful like you, think of it!"

"I think it is my son. I wouldn't have minded a son. I'd always keep the sons. How old is he Johnnie?"

"She's eight weeks."

"Isn't he just perfect!"

"Yes. There's only one thing wrong with her."

"There's not a thing wrong with him!"

"She's dead that's all."

"That doesn't matter. You should be glad he is. Think of the awkward consequences."

"I'd give my right hand if I could put her back; the one I operate with."

"Ooh don't be so gloomy, we're awfully clever. Look at my cute wee Baal."

"What I can't understand is . . . is how it happened. I *can't* understand that part."

"Don't tell me there was a flaw in your technique."

"There was never a margin of chance as far as I knew."

" 'S funny all right."

"I suppose . . . you did tell me you were sick didn't you? I suppose that was it."

"I thought I had gastric flu. That's what you told me."

"I still can't understand it. I've been sitting here thinking of it, going over everything, waiting for you to come round."

Silence. I lie back on my pillows and turn my face away.

"Me of all people . . . a doctor!"

"Never mind. It's over. Forget about it."

"No I won't forget about it. But you can thank your lucky stars there's no other man in this story. Otherwise I . . ."

I lurch up in bed. "Of course there's no other man in this story! How can you say such a thing! There's never been another man in this story! Or in any other story! There's only been you. People like me wouldn't dream of . . ." I stop suddenly and whisper, "Don't look at me like that!"

"So that's it."

"Don't look at me like that . . . you frighten me!"

He rises and packs his bag, his bent back to me, and doesn't reply.

"Johnnie don't leave me I need you!"

"God what a fool I've been!"

"Johnnie I'm sick. You've got to stay with me!"

"Hold your tongue till I get out of here!"

"Why should you care . . . you don't love me. You've always left your soul at home with your wife!" He turns, still bent, the romance departed from his face then straightens and swings on his heel. I whisper after him, "Don't leave your kid here with me."

Back he lunges and snatches the glass and shouts, "Have you no respect for life! Or death! Is there any feeling in you at all but for yourself! By God I could thrash you too! You . . . !"

"You what? Go on. Make it good."

"You common little Continental cheat!"

"Not bad . . . your own?"

"Do you know what you are! Cheeky! Just a damned cheeky spoilt little devil!"

I laugh. "That's what my father said."

153

"I can thoroughly understand someone smacking your be-hind! It doesn't take a genius to see it was a man about my age!"

"It took a genius to smack it though. But you use the word genius too loosely. It should not be used more than twice a century."

"By God!" he lifts a fist. "I'll . . . !"

"If you're going to smack my bottom too postpone it a little will you? In the interests of my practise. I'm already un-able to sit. I'm getting behind with my thirds."

He snatches an arm, pulls me half from bed then suddenly, passionately holds me. "My girl . . . you're so soft . . . this heavenly fragrance . . ." He sits on the side of the bed stifling me in his arms. The soft rain in the dawn . . . we are very close. All sorts of inner horizons reveal themselves; these mysterious areas of sentiment of yours unfamiliar to people like me. A close time with men, the dawn, don't you think? Or don't you know anything about it? He kisses my bare arms both of them then all over my face.

"I could have done with a father like you Johnnie. You're just like a father sometimes. Are you what real fathers are like? Kind ones I mean?"

He whispers, "I wish I were your father. I wish you were my daughter. If you'd been mine I'd never have let this hap-pen to you. I've never had a daughter until this morning . . . in that long-stemmed wineglass. She may be mine." He pulls the eiderdown and wraps it about me. "If only you would be a good girl as though you were my beautiful loving daughter."

"It wouldn't have been so hard to be a good girl if I had been your daughter. You would have given me a loving recep-tion when I was born like that one in the glass. My own reception was anything but lovely. My mother died when I was born you know, at birth. They gave me to my father a minute old. He was at the piano playing. He put me on top

154

of the pianoforte and went on playing. And that's where I stayed all my babyhood waking and sleeping. I lived on that grand; I heard every note. There was no woman there, he cared for me himself. The sound of the music has not left me till this day. I hear music all the time; everything from chansons through hymns to jukeboxes. I can hear it this very minute; I hear a chanson 'May the night bear my breath away.' I can relieve myself only by playing. I'm not a real musician; I don't really love music. It's music that loves me."

"Is that the reason for all that listening?"

"I try to hide it; I hate it."

"You should have told me all this before."

"Why? You can't operate it out or pethidine it out."

Silence for a while and the rain. I lie closer to him. "I might have been a good girl had I had a mummie to love me; or even a daddy to love me. But I've got to get other men to love me. I can't get women to love me; goodness knows why. And I always aim at men much older. That's how the whole thing works. Illustration of a girl in search of parents. Pathetic n'est-ce pas?"

"You'll have to look out for that Frenchman . . . with his violence. Wasn't there something about him in Paris . . ."

"Ooh he's all right. I just said the wrong thing."

"What did you say may I ask?"

"I only said 'Don't touch me' that's all."

"A little late wasn't it?"

I smile into his Mammony coat. "We're used to action in Paris."

"Prudence and tact are not virtues of the French." Pause . . . "Now we've got to put you back and keep you warm. I wish this illness was something I could call in a nurse to. I don't know what the devil I'm going to do." He tucks me back quite professionally, blankets right up to the chin. "If

155

only you would keep yourself just for me alone Germaine."

"À quoi bon? You don't take me out. I couldn't confine my life to your brief, hurried visits. I need someone who can take me to public concerts and . . ."

He lifts his hands from me and stands back. "So that's who it was . . . Montigny; that outsider." He glances at the glass near the bed. "Montigny's child. The sort of thing you'd expect to happen to a child of his."

"As a matter of fact he's yours; I happen to know. I should have said so before."

"Are you sure about that darling?"

"Dead certain. Cute isn't he? Just like a wee idol with his knees tucked up. A little baby Baal. What'll we call him?"

"Don't talk with such levity there's a limit."

"Where are you going to bury him then?"

"Please Germaine be gentle; a little more mature. Can't you sense the feelings of others? I'm a very sad man."

"I just can't see why. You've had a lucky let-off. Doesn't matter he's dead. All that matters is the . . . the felicity part. He is only a physical accident."

"You know quite well that it took more than a physical accident to give her life in the first place. If you remember."

I do remember and blush to do so. "I still think you should stop being sad."

"I've a reason to be sad to bury my daughter." He sits on the bed and turns away his face. The first birdcall rings. "I must go. Germaine, you'll have to agree to something. I'm too busy to nurse you. I'm going to send a Maori woman from the village. Ruth; she's a dear. Maoris understand these things. They're full of sympathy and can be trusted. Ruth has two long black plaits like you . . . not so long, and not so sleek. She goes round in bare feet summer and winter. She can get your wood and feed you and nurse you and . . ."

"I'd like you better Johnnie."

"It's impossible pet. Be a good girl and do what I say."

"I will if you promise me something." I play with the silver

156

stars on the bodice of the black nylon nightie. "If ever I . . . if ever anyone's . . . if ever your . . . aa . . . your technique failed again would you . . ."

He quite changes. "You forget you're in New Zealand. I'm a New Zealand doctor."

"Don't be silly Johnnie."

"If respect for life is silly then I'll remain a fool."

"But what'll I do?"

"Turn your positive thinking on it."

"Well for God's sake repair your technique!"

"You could well overhaul your own."

He stands a moment at the door before he goes, his daughter in his hand. "What did your father have against you?"

"He said I killed my mother."

"I see."

I say nothing and trace the silver stars with a finger and he looks at his daughter in the wineglass. "I'm a very sad man."

"Well stay and talk to me. Just till morning comes. I'd make you some coffee if you'd let me. Pull the heater nearer. Sit on that old pink chair. There's some wine in the cupboard by the window. Don't go till morning . . . I don't like being my own boss when I'm sick. It's an exhausting business. It's . . . sort of . . . sort of solitary when you don't love anybody. I've been feeling funny lately. I feel like something drifting . . . I haven't got the words. I mean I . . . I'm a single separated petal; I see myself floating by on dark threatening waters."

"If your baby had lived you wouldn't have felt like that. You would have been attached for good."

"I wish now I'd known. A nice sort of doctor you are! Not picking someone straight out pregnant! If I'd known . . . I wonder. All those weeks I wasn't on my own. And I didn't know it . . . now don't you start making me feel sorry! Talking like that."

"I can't see you being sorry about anything."

157

If he'd been yours mon cher I'd be sorry. . . .

"As for me not picking it," he says, "you didn't give me all the facts."

But men always go . . . however much they love you, unless you are married to them. When the slow morning at last wakes, stretching and yawning in its feel of blossom, this one goes too. Lying alone in my wide bed I am equal to only one simple conclusion: that the physical touch, whether in passion, compassion or thrashing has little to do with real union, of the deathless kind the Villain speaks of; there's something else I don't know about. When Johnnie has gone and Ruth has come I am still where I was at the very beginning before Gordon Hood arrived. After an evening and a night and a dawn with five men in sequence I'm not in the slightest bit different; I remain a single petal floating by on waters unfathomed.

I understand this whole drink containing the ingredients of men . . . ooh so little. I understand it as little as I understood an outrageous composition of Léon's he played one recent dawn; a confusion of isolated phrases scattered over a chart which you played in any sequence you wished; each phrase in itself enigmatic. And you began on whichever particular one the eye fell upon first and followed with whichever one your eye fell on next. And some of it was played on the keyboard and some on the open strings. Can you imagine it, mon cher. How could such as you and I understand such as that. Ultra-sophistication . . . "But what does it mean to you," I said. "It doesn't have to mean anything," he said. "I love sound as sound alone. Let it dissolve on the air."

I turn my face to the wall for some sleep with a hand over my eyes floating by on waters unfathomed as men pound me with their personalities . . .

waters unfathomed . . .

waters.

Litany to Baal . . .

"O toi, le plus savant et le plus beau des Anges
Dieu trahi par le sort et privé de louanges . . .

Toi qui . . .
Enseignes par l'amour le goût du Paradis . . ."

NYWAY! How ARE you!"

I throw up my hands from the keyboard.

"I waited outside, I waited outside for a while."

Oooh . . . my hand!

"H'm?" You take a chair at the table. "How are you?"

"I–I . . . I don't know . . . ever."

"You don't know, you don't know . . . h'm."

"Do you ever know?"

"H'm . . . ?"

"I mean how you are. Do you ever know . . . how you are?"

"Oh . . . how *I* am? I think so I think so. I'm well. H'm yes. I'm well enough."

"Oh . . . how . . . how interesting."

"Do you think so?"

"What did you say?"

"Do you think so?"

"Think what?"

"Do you think it is interesting that I should know how I am?"

"Oh I see what you mean. Yes I . . . I think that's . . . that's interesting."

Pause.

"You must know how you are."

"If I did I . . . I wouldn't say. I never say how I am it's . . . boring."

Smile. You reach forward a long arm and an ill-built hand and turn the face of the daffodil towards you and examine its nervous soul, it squirms like anything poor thing.

"I'm . . . just going to make a drink sir. I . . . always have one after practise before I—I go for my walk in the orchards. Will you have something with me? Or have you already had something on your . . . I suppose you get . . . people must offer you something on your rounds."

"I haven't had anything so far."

How can I go to the mirror . . . what about my face! My hair I haven't done it today. Where are the Aladdin slippers with the gold paintings? What's different about you . . . ooh tweed suit instead of the black. Grey of course but still the clerical collar. What shall I say next? Mon Dieu I need a drink! "Or would you rather have wine?"

"Tea today thank you tea. After last night not wine."

You take up the latest chanson "May the night bear my breath away." You have already borne it away.

"You New Zealanders like your tea."

"We New Zealanders like our tea . . . h'm. H'm. This is an extraordinary manuscript. Do composers generally write all over it like this? There's so much you know that I don't. All this music . . ."

"A madman writes that music." What's banging in my

162

throat, some organ out of place? Is this my heart up here
. . . what's thumping in the middle then? Mon Dieu I
must have wine!

"And how's it all going anyway, all this music?"

"In my own way." Which cups shall I use? Where's the
damned teapot? Have I got any milk . . . no.

"Anyway it's good for you. Even without a purpose. Whichever way you look at it it must be good for you. It must
thoroughly extend you. It would supply all you need."

"Not quite all." Careless that. A fearful silence full of
thought in undress. This decanter is empty, there must be
more wine in the cabinet. Don't tell me there's no . . .

"And how much time do you put into it each day?"

"I can't stand any more questions!"

Pause. You put on your emergency look, innocent and
blameless. Soft . . . "I have not yet found the right formula
for visiting you apparently."

"I can't stand formulae either!" I pour the Rhône wine
and drink it all. I pour some more and drink this too. You're
the man who called me a fool . . . "I can't stand conversation at all! Not at this time of day!"

"There are times when I can't either."

Silence.

You reach forward and lay the back of your ungainly
fingers on my cheek stroking a little. "There are times
when I can't either."

Silence.

"You don't look well Mrs. Jones."

"It's—it's . . . after being with the masters all day I . . .
my own talk seems so trivial, too trivial afterwards."

"That could well be. After being with an alcoholic all
night *my* talk seems too trivial afterwards." You close the
chansons and lean back with a yawn. "It's quiet out here.
No bells, no traffic, no jukebox. Lovely . . ."

At last the wine begins its incomparable softening process

finding all the tense places undoing knots coaxing organs back home . . . I sink into the nearest chair. "It all depends when you're here. In a storm it's not quiet it's rowdy in a storm. Too loud the trees too loud . . . fortissimo . . . scherzando . . ."

"I got rid of all mine."

Silence. The daffodil on the table in her long-necked crystal vase with the late afternoon sun through her petals, the sun catching the rims of the china and glancing on the silver teapot, my grand pianoforte lying open and my grand bed lying shut, the sun reaching me and the sun reaching you . . . slowly tentatively I offer my eyes then at once withdraw them again. "You should rest for a while Mr. Guymer."

"Bless you indeed for that."

"How do you like your tea sir strong or weak?"

"Strong, strong. Please, I should add."

"Milk?"

"No. No milk."

"Sugar of course. All men take sugar."

"ALL MEN TAKE SUGAR."

"Good title for a sermon. Women don't of course."

"No?"

"Not women with any sense. Dress sense . . . I mean."

"I hadn't noticed."

"You haven't noticed women."

"I'm afraid I haven't."

"I HAVEN'T NOTICED WOMEN. Another good title."

"H'm. I could do with some original titles."

"Could you deliver a sermon on that sir? About not noticing women? What would you say on that?"

You weigh a lot of thinking to yourself, and a lot of smiles too, but don't say one damned thing.

164

"You haven't said one d . . . one thing."

"Babylon would like a title like that."

"I say I hope you don't want anything to eat sir. I don't go in for smart things in tins like proper women." "Proper" is a mistake.

"Oh no no. I must watch your weight . . . aa my—MY weight." Ill-chosen that word. . . .

"YOUR weight. But here are some rolls I made; a Continental recipe. I had to do something about the food out here."

"So you CAN cook?"

"Of course I can. I'm ordinary enough to cook."

Smile. You glance at my Aladdin slippers and then at my hands and sip your tea reflectively.

"You're weighing some words," I accuse.

A wider smile then a yawn.

"Whenever I see a man yawn I know he's been called out on his rounds at night."

"My rounds came to me . . . CAME TO ME! . . . last night."

"If you've had an attack of rounds last night you will not have done any today."

"I did some today, I did some today." You examine your empty cup. "There were several up at the hospital to see today." You pass me back your cup.

"The hospital can hardly be a pick-me-up."

"Not like a cup of strong tea." Yawn . . . "I try to take it in my stride you know. I try to remember that the body is something wonderful, the habitation of the soul. But walking through those wards . . . THOSE WARDS! . . . I forget it all. Yes . . ." you stroke your mouth in the way I know, "I forget it. Up there I see the body as no more than a receptacle of all kinds of agonies and subject to decay . . . subject to decay. I have a young woman there at the moment, a young woman, not expected to live although I will see . . . I WILL SEE! . . . that she does . . . youth. Youth," you look at the daffodil, "it comes like a flash of lightning only to be followed by the thunderclap of grief." You reach an absent hand for your cup. "Youth . . ." you find my own eyes, "it's like lightning in the brain."

I receive your eyes and hold them in mine as long as I can bear it then drink two glasses of wine to get over it and lie back in the pink chair in the sun and close them upon myself. "Forget the thunder sir; think of the lightning."

"Bless you again for that."

I think the church is dropping off you a bit except for the clerical collar. What with the grey suit and your brief talk of yourself here is this down-to-earth man of men I have suspected for many a Sunday. As you stare down through the floor at your favourite meditating place I risk a look at your face; a face that looks older in the daylight with many other lives trampled over it.

I confess I relax too and not wholly from the wine. With anyone else I would be open about how I feel and lie horizontal somewhere. But I still feel easier about you. Tired quiet men in my studio are not aggressive preachers in a church. If you were more like this on Sunday evenings church would prove less expensive. Not that you have relaxed yourself. Pushing away your cup and lifting back your chair up you get and begin pacing; reconnoitring at first. There's not much room for really effective pacing in here what with a grand pianoforte and a grand bed too but it seems that you need to and you organise for yourself a route. Sometimes you look up to the embarrassment of the spiders and at others bore through the floor, pacing in a pent way as though there were something within to control. But I'm the last to be able to sense the essence of a man and it's manual labour trying.

166

The innocent glance and on with the pacing. "This young chap rang me up about twelve. Midnight. He said he had to see me that minute so I told him to come round. He DID come round. He had just drunk five bottles of wine to get to me."

Five bottles of wine! That makes the rest of us teetotallers.

"He told me everything. He seemed to feel better so when he could stand I let him go. But about half an hour afterwards a friend of his rang and asked if he could bring him back again. It seems that when he left me he went straight back to the wine." You return to the table and lift a foot on your chair. "All I could do from there was to keep him from drinking any more. Which meant that I rang a friend of MINE to come and give me a hand. And I mean a hand; both." You pause a moment reflecting. "You see he's got money. He's a casual hand on the wharf. Strictly casual of course."

"Doesn't he live anywhere, belong to a family or something?"

"He lives in his car, a Jowett-Javelin." You take out a tin of tobacco and begin on rolling a cigarette. "Somehow we've got to keep him out of this car otherwise he will end up, not in the ministry, but in gaol."

"The *ministry!*"

"Men with worse starts have made it."

"But does he *want* to enter the ministry?"

"There's no pressure from me. We haven't even discussed it. But a passionate atheist, as he went to some pains to let me know he was, betrays a passionate interest in religion. This boy's born to preaching, both in temperament and disposition. A passionate anything reveals much to me. Christ chose his disciples from passionate anythings. He had a use for the passion. So," you lift your glance to me, "has the church a use for passion." You deliberately find my eyes, "All kinds." I look away from you and you continue: "And the way he

167

has sat on my church steps for so long reveals much else to me."

"What," I ask the flame in the grate, "do you plan to do with him?"

You light up. "He won't be the first I have taken into the parsonage with me. Not by any means. Neither will he be the last. The parsonage can take it; it's a pretty solid house."

"What about when he wants a drink? Can you fight?"

"I defended myself last night all right."

"He must have some people somewhere."

"I believe there are but I don't see myself finding them. Hugh can earn his own funds. He's quite capable of paying his own way through Varsity." The pacing resumes and one hand finds a pocket. "All I can do is keep him with me. While he's with me he won't drink."

"You'll have to leave him sometimes, sir. What about your rounds and services and meetings and your own personal life?" What about, I don't add, your wife.

You pull up at the table again. "I see no reason why he should not accompany me into my personal life . . . such as it is. It would at least be better than working on the wharf and sleeping in the car eating nothing and drinking EVERY-THING. Don't you think?" The blameless glance. "AND driving the car when drunk." Off again on the pacing.

"What makes you think he will come?"

"He'll come."

"Will he?"

"I have faith in him and he knows it. Which is what was missing before."

"What will Babylon say?"

Return of your old belligerence. "I'm always ready to take on Babylon." You pull up at the table at last as though from an arduous journey and stroke your face in that way I know. "The pain in this world . . . the pain in this world. Is there any direction from which the cries of suffering do not come."

168

"Your work seems to extend you sir."

"Extend me!" You rub your face all over. "It extends me beyond any life of my own."

"You don't have a life of your own?"

"My own life?"

"You live one don't you?"

"This longing at times for my own life. My own house furniture garden. My own time, my own inclinations, my own . . ." you weigh the next words I notice, "my own appetites." Another interesting silence. "My own WAY," you add with emphasis.

I pour some more wine I need it. Wine never weighs words. "Your own way in what?"

"My own way in interpreting God."

"Why, in whose way do you interpret him now?"

"In the way . . . IN THE WAY! . . . I'm expected."

"Why not your own?"

You use the chair for its original purpose and sit squarely upon it, and lean back full of a sigh. "I don't know my own way yet. And if I did . . . I'd be afraid."

The wine weighs this for a change. It also weighs your eyes. With fine white wine supporting me I lie in yours for a long time. And even go on staying there without leaving. I whisper "I don't think you're afraid Mr. Guymer."

"Bless you," softly, "for that."

There's nothing new in a man resting here. They all do automatically. Respectability seems to be a heavy burden and they all cast it in time. No doubt the magistrate would too. On the mat, on the pink chair, on the bed but you on a straight chair at the table. You rest in detumescence for I feel the pressure gone. Men always express themselves first with me and when they no longer do I drop them. I know I should make my response now, it's my turn, but for some reason I can't to you. In any case I always absent myself when a man is resting; it's private like sleeping or eating. I long to stretch out myself but how can I with you powerfully here? It would be easier to lie on the railway line. It's the sense of sin I think, that everything I do is . . . I rise and drift off and away to the keyboard. . . .

There seems little relation now between the reverend I bring home feverishly from church and this stark male resting here. Your clothes are no longer a . . . marvellous passage here in this chanson . . . what was I thinking? Your clothes. They're no longer a dark setting for your voice but a common grey texture bought by the yard and cut by the swift hands of a tailor cheerfully earning his crust. Cheerfully earning his . . . this passage is ultra-sophistication . . . his what? Nor is your face now some futuristic painting in oils in the drama and lights of a church flashing shadow and light but a contemporary work in flesh flashing nothing at all. Even the cadences of . . . my hands slow to a stop and my fingers come to rest on the foreboard . . . cadences I was thinking. Even the cadences of speech and the sanctities of word are slain in this broad bald daylight. No dazzling deliria flame to spark the religious fervour; no fierce updraught of the spirit forces you to the stars. In this unvaulted, un-pewed un-anthemed studio concerned with affairs mortal you are no lover and perfect equal mon cher, picking me out by secret and divine signs. I feel I'm housing a stranger. But a stranger who is more convincing. Much more valid the man than metaphor. . . .

"You haven't checked on my sins sir."
"Neither have you on mine."
"*Yours!*"
"Mine."
"But . . . but you don't burn incense to idols."
"Why, do you?"
"I think so sometimes . . . in church."

170

"Do you?"

Your eyes in mine reconnoitre.

I don't answer.

"Do you?"

Silence.

Still the reconnoitring.

I say at length "You hardly approve of us."

Smile . . . it's over. "It may not be I who hardly approve."

"I thought I was on your tough visiting list."

You laugh aloud it's lovely! "What else have you been thinking?"

"About those exams."

"You did hear me then?"

"I heard you all too well. Last Sunday I . . . was . . . was . . . untroubled. I . . . someone brought me to church that night."

You still smile to yourself and say nothing. All this saying nothing . . . I've had enough of it. "If there's anything I can't stand it's discretion!"

Roars of earthy and bodily laughter then you rise. "H'm. Well I must be going. ANYWAY! . . . thank you for all the listening."

"I can't get up to see you off."

You stand tall above me and I . . .

"I hope this is not serious."

"It's something I don't talk about."

Another man standing before me with all this magic of masculinity . . . my downfall always. The tweed, the shape, the breath, the man odour . . . don't go away mon cher. . . .

"How do you manage living alone?"

Pause. "I'm not ashamed of my single state."

"Neither am I of mine."

"*Yours!*"

"I live alone too."

"*You* do! I didn't know I . . ."

171

"Do you have a broom Mrs. Jones?"

"A *broom!* . . ."

You find it on the porch and begin on the hysterical spiders. "Traditionalists!" you blaze beneath your breath. "Ecclesiasticists!"

"Don't let them fall on my bed!"

"Orthodoxists . . . conformists . . . ritualists! . . ."

"Look out for my clothes! And my picture of the Seine!"

"Now where's the brush and shovel!"

Here is the pulpit voice back again in all its original magnificence, and once more your fingers on my face and the length of the church between us. "Anyway!" you stroke me, "bless you."

HERE IS GORDON HOOD on Saturday afternoon in dungarees and sweat. He has a scythe, a spade, a rake and an axe and what else? All upon a truck and he is cheerfully unshaven. There is no honey'd morphine or mystic delirium about him, no capital letters in his speech, he doesn't pace and he costs me nothing in cocktails. He is not concerned whether your religious sentiment is secondhand or matured, he views idolatry lightly and he never mentions one's whoredom from under one's God. He's the kind of Christian to be endured. He engages himself mainly with one's outer life, never referring to one's inner and is damned good apéritif after you.

"What's your hand bound up for Mr. Hood?"

"Gordon's my name on Saturday."

"Gordon. And the sticking plaster on your face?"

"You might well ask."

"What happened?"

He laughs, "It's nothing. I was giving Brett a hand with a joker and we ran into a little action. It seems he wanted a drink."

"What's a joker?"

He laughs again. "In this case it was a young chap. You should have seen old Brett. He's no fool in a fight. He didn't get a scratch and look at *me!*"

"Was it the young man on the steps on Sunday?"

"Oh yes of course you know him. He'll need some repairs too as well as the parsonage. Now how's this old building, all right? No draughts, leaks or anything?"

"The Reverend Guymer said something about taking that boy into the parsonage with him. Is that the same one?"

"Oh Brett goes beyond his duty. There's no need to take him into the parsonage. I'm taking him into my firm."

There's a calm about Gordon Hood, not just overlay. There's integration in the look and the presence of him. He must be making her an admirable husband; another conforming New Zealander she'll be, breeding and spreading and fading without the slightest knowledge of Style. Most good men are bad choosers and all the best are married . . . I brush away the tides of music within; "What did you say?"

"That guttering up there must be full of leaves after the winter gales. I don't see how the down-pipes can be working at all. Have you noticed? Look at the height of those three trees! Faith, Hope and Charity . . . are the down-pipes working?"

You can pick them a mile off, married men. There's an absence of tension in them of those who know the worst. No surplus emotion or not too much. They leave their souls home with their wives. You can tell them anything, talk about anything and behave how you like. Shockproof is the word I'd use . . . "Sorry what were you saying?"

174

"I was wondering what you were doing for wood. A cold place this in the spring. You haven't been cold have you?" But the music surges on; there's no fierce awareness to wrench me out of it as there is when I'm with you. I listen comfortably inward; a crescendo is delaying pace. . . .

"Have you been cold?"

"Cold, let me think." I brush my eyes. "I believe I have been." I haven't but you can't waste good married men; not a kind one like this one anyway. Bachelors by comparison are useless which brings me once more to speculating on you.

"Have you got any wood chopped for tonight?"

"Wood for tonight . . . wood for tonight . . . oh did you say wood for tonight?" Wood and chansons; doesn't he know what hands are for? "There's still some pieces the carpenters left."

"H'm I'd better have a load of cut timber ends delived." He looks down upon me. "I wonder you survive on your own."

"It's not always easy."

He looks at me a moment longer, at the flowered skirt in C Major and the Swiss shoes that lace up the ankle. "We'll have to do something about it." Then he returns to the chaos about us. "Crikey! This place wants an overhaul doesn't it!"

"I could do with a few flowers. I must buy some in Babylon."

"There'll have to be a rotary hoe in first."

"What's a rotary hoe?"

"A sort of plough."

"A plough? What, wheels and that?"

"And an engine."

"Not an engine! Oh no, Gordon leave it like this! I'll find a corner here and there for a flower."

"I'll have to get hold of that rotary hoe. There's one at the orchard."

"What orchard?"

"One of those orchards along the road is mine."

"I thought you had a business in town."

"I have two businesses in town as well. You've got to do something with your time. Yes this place needs the hoe."

"Oh no! It must be very noisy. Leave it like this."

"I'm likely to."

"All I need is a hollyhock at the door and a pansy or two looking up."

"I'm jolly sure nothing is going to look up in this wilderness."

"I manage to."

He smiles down upon me and speaks of something else. "We'll just have to begin on the things nearest to hand and work outwards. As they crop up. I'll start on this track to the gate. To be frank I don't know how you get in and out. How do you get the car out?"

"I just mix a cocktail, shut my eyes, and find myself on the road."

"I can well believe it."

"I always make a point of opening my eyes once I'm on the road."

"Well done. But just in case you fail to open them on the road ever again, one of these days I'll clear and widen it." He heads off round the studio with me trailing after him. "You've never," he remarks, "thought of buying a wheelbarrow?"

"Who me . . . a wheelbarrow?"

"Do you know what a wheelbarrow is? Never mind I'll bring one next time. There's a consignment coming in next week, God willing and license permitting. And some of them are small," he smiles down at me, "about your weight. Now," he still gazes upon me . . . "we'll make a start."

"I ought to make you some coffee first, tea I mean. I'd have made you some biscuits manqué, the recipe they use in the Deux Magots on the Boulevard Saint-Germain . . . before it became overtouristy . . . but I've blown the oven."

"You have? Have you done anything about it?"

"Me?"

"I'll send one of my men to fix it."

"I can still use the top of the stove, and my New Zealand pikelets are coming right."

"There's my girl! She's going to make me some pikelets!"

"And then I'll call you in."

"I love being called in for tea." A lovely smile; whiskers and all. "But don't go for a moment. I'll need a hand with this branch."

"I'll get some gloves."

"Go on, this won't hurt you."

"I must . . ."

"Why," I ask later as we work together, he scything and I carrying away to the heap, "are the congregations so big at church these days?"

"I'm not quite sure. There's one thing certain, it's not the sermons."

"That's what made me wonder."

"I have a theory. People like the sensation of finding fault and our minister is a wonderful target. I've heard the comments outside afterwards and when I take over some of his rounds. They say some very cruel things. I doubt if he's as bad as the city thinks he is though. If they'd seen him handle that boy last night . . ."

"He wouldn't have been able to do that sort of thing if he'd had a wife and family."

"No. Is this branch too heavy for you?"

"Not if you take the end of it."

"That's why he didn't marry; to give all of himself to his work."

"I thought it was because he didn't notice women."

"He treats men and women alike. If Hugh last night had

177

been a girl he would still have taken her into the parsonage, just the same."

"But what would Babylon say?"

"He wouldn't care, I think."

"You don't need to take off that branch; I don't hit that branch."

"I can't be sure that you won't. You can't go on living a charmed life."

"Why can't I? I think I'll go in now. And make those . . ."

"I've tired you . . . Mrs. Jones."

"Germaine."

He continues pulling at the branch and doesn't answer.

"I'll make those pikelets now. My hands have had enough. My arms too. Then I'll call you for tea . . . Gordon." And also powder my face. Don't forget there's an extra window I want put in to light the piano more . . . and the oven fixed of course and a reading light by my bed and a shower put in the bathroom and as I said before you don't waste good married men and another thing I'd better go to church again after all. . . .

"It's been so nice to have you here, Gordon," I say much later as he loads up his truck, "I don't feel sinful with you about."

"That's a strange thing to say . . . Germaine."

"It's a strange thing to feel."

"It's new to hear you talk like that; you didn't before."

"I didn't feel it before."

"You mustn't take his sermons too seriously. No one else does. The city treats them as a joke."

I sigh, a long one. "I don't seem to be able to think of anything else . . . except about being sinful."

He pauses and weighs his words. "I don't think you're sinful. No more than the rest of us are. Anyone as lovely as you . . . couldn't be."

"Thank you Gordon."

"Don't take too much notice of what he says. Not as much as you are."

"I don't seem to be able to help it. Never mind it was nice to see you."

"I must get home to those babies of mine. Bathing time and feeding and putting to bed is heavy on my mother."

"Where's your wife?"

"She's up at hospital . . . again."

"Oh."

"She'll be there for a while I think. Brett is with her this afternoon. He never misses a day. He never lets a day go by without saying to her 'Bless you.' "

"Who's Gordon Hood Johnnie?"

"The richest joker in town. Come here pet I've only got a minute."

"Where does he live?"

"In the latest in palaces on the hill; Gordon's Monument we call it. He built it from fruit and ironmongery and commission on spraying machines. He throws money round like a man with four arms . . . on himself of course. Y'know y'know I can never work out how a business tycoon like Dalgliesh and a fruit baron like Hood . . . how they can reconcile their wealth with Christianity. Can a camel get through the eye of a needle these days? I . . ."

"Isn't his wife your . . ."

". . . I think the poor old maligned Government shows more Christianity in the savage way they tax them. Did you see in the paper the other day where . . ."

"Is Mrs. Hood your . . ."

". . . where one of them got caught? Evading income tax? At 'em boys! Look if I had what Hood's spending on his new Cool Store I'd build myself a private hospital."

"Johnnie isn't Mrs. Hood your patient?"

Pause. "Yes."

"What's the matter with her Johnnie?"

"My pet . . . I don't discuss my patients. You know it. Come here . . . Germaine . . ."

"I'll come if you tell me what's the matter with Mrs. Hood."

"She's dying . . . or should be; there's not a show."

"What does that mean . . . 'There's not a show'?"

"Oh . . ." he laughs. "It means 'She hasn't got a chance.' New Zealandese."

"Does he know?"

"No." A long deep sigh. "I think I'll break my rule and have some wine. No . . . no not all that! It's something I can't face telling him. She'd read it in him for certain. No husband can successfully keep anything like that from his wife for long. There's an unspoken language between us . . . between us and our wives. How can a chap coldly tell him when they've got three little kiddies? A girl of two or three . . . how old is little Corinne now? About that; I remember when I delivered her . . . and these twin baby boys. I'll get that parson of yours to tell him, he's with her every day." He drinks a long wine so unusual for him on call. I think there is something else worrying him. "I can't pull her round . . . but he might. I always honour the hundredth chance. Whatever he calls his treatment is keeping up the hope in her, her faith in life, the will to live. She says to me 'I'm not sick Doctor. I'm not sick at all. I'm not going to die. I'm going to live for my little ones.' You can do with that in a patient. Then she says 'God wouldn't take me now. He gave me my little babies. And he gave me my Gordon.' What can a chap do in the face of that? Tell her husband she's doomed? I tell you there's a place for Brett Guymers. Oh do come here darling. Just for a moment before I go. I'm too tired to go chasing round after you. Let's skip the courting. Come on drop the technique . . . Germaine . . ."

"I suppose Johnnie that if . . . you say married people

180

can read each other . . . how much I wonder. Could one read the other was . . . unfaithful?"

"Who are you talking about!"

"I was thinking of . . ."

"If you're thinking of me and Mrs. John . . . ! You're hardly a queen of tact!"

"I wasn't! I was not Johnnie I . . ."

"I spoke to you before about that sort of thing . . . about the unwritten boundary. There's . . ."

"But I wasn't thinking of you I . . . I wasn't I tell you! I . . . it's just the kind of general thing that . . . that any-one would wonder. I . . ."

"For God's sake don't lets quarrel! Come here."

"How long would Mrs. Hood be likely to live if she . . . if she lost this faith of hers in life . . . in God I mean? I'll . . . come and kiss you . . . if you tell me."

"You're like all women with your nagging! What the devil do you want to know for!"

"What are you so bad-tempered for lately? I don't want you if you're bad-tempered with me. I can do without *you* Doctor John! Why don't you get up and go now . . . for good? I'll manage to survive. Go on . . . go!"

"How dare you talk to me like that you cheeky little devil!"

"You keep your antiseptic discipline where it belongs in the theatre!"

"Don't answer me back!"

"Since when have you been my boss? Keep your orders for your nurses and patients. I'll live in my own way."

"Have you no respect for your elders! Have you no respect for anyone or anything! A wildcat has better manners! What sort of bringing-up have you had! If *any*! I've met better brought up, better behaved, better bred gamins in the gutters of the Latin Quarter! What *you* need is . . . !"

"Don't get overheated Doctor. It's operating day tomor-row."

". . . a *damn good hiding!* And *I'm* the one who'll do it this time! By God I'll . . . !"

"You boorish Néo-Zélandais. You insular, wool-brained, mutton-bred, butter-spread . . . rugby-mad . . . beer-blind antipodean!"

"You cunning little Continental cheat! Don't you insult my country!"

"Your country? Call this a country? Where everything from fashion to morals is respectably factory-cut? Where the Style is three years behind my country and the morality five hundred? Insult your country what a joke! How can you insult a country whose heart-beat is the price of wool!"

"Then why-the-devil-don't-you-get-out-of-it!"

"In my own good time I *will* get out of it. Your government has sliced enough of my income. All those hard-earned royalties of mine . . . to keep your Welfare State! I'm tired of financing your social security!"

Soft . . . shocked . . . money. Whisper, "They're not taxing you short are they dear!"

"The taxes are bad enough! It's the forms you've got to fill in! I followed a countryman of mine out here to advance my music technique; not to study trigonometry and higher mathematics!"

Roars of hefty laughter. Suddenly he engulfs me, crushes . . . stifles . . . "My pet my love my beautiful! My glorious little daughter! Let's not quarrel sweetheart! I've got enough to worry me! My lovely lovely Germaine . . . I can't I *can't* do without you! I . . ."

"I can't breathe Johnnie . . ."

"Tell me you still love me darling . . . tell me you still want me!"

"I can't I've got no breath . . ."

"I can't do without you Germaine however much I try. I can't let you go Germaine. I tell you I cannot."

"Of course you can. You haven't tried."

"No Germaine no. A man must have some glamour in his

life, some mystery, some beauty. How can a man like me living among those in pain all day do without some spark of . . . I mean something, something wonderful . . . I . . ."

"The Reverend Guymer says that God should supply all that. God does supply that for him . . . the way he goes on. He's madly in love with God."

"Y-yes . . . that's a thought . . . but why bring *him* up at this moment? Does he mean anything to you?"

"He makes me sick."

"Do I make you sick?"

"You? *You* made me sick all right. I haven't got over it *yet!* Oh well . . . so Gordon's the richest man in town and lives in a palace on the hill and throws money round like a man with four arms . . . on himself and . . ." Well you'd never have thought so last Saturday.

The Clock Tower rising tall white and regal above the flattened crouching earthquake-fearing business area like the terrible and beautiful princess of Jerusalem before her fall that I hear about in church. Gleaming in the spring sunlight and proud. As she peals regularly her eleven strokes I pause beneath her. In my hand is a large blue hyacinth I have bought like the ones from the street stalls in Notre-Dame but round her feet are blooming daffodils, jonquils, ranunculi, anemones, primulas and pansies as well as all colours of hyacinth. I pause for a moment beneath her while the city people in their grey national uniforms and cardigans and skirts and permed hair and the famous "get-along" walk endlessly cross and recross the railway line that cuts Babylon in half like the Seine . . . "There's my girl!" A hand grips my arm. . . .

It turns out to be all too easy to get Gordon Hood talking

about his children, raving is rather the word. "You should hear Corinne saying her prayers last night. Every night when I hear her she's got some good reason why not everyone should be blessed. Or not at once anyway. Crikey she's a cute little kid! I said to her last night, 'Say Pray God make me a good girl.'

"And she said 'Pray God make me a good girl. No, Brett make me a good girl.'

"I said 'Bless Grandma.'

"And she said 'No bless you first.'

" 'All right' I said 'Bless me.'

" 'Yes, yes bless G'anma' she said.

" 'Bless Daddy' I said.

" 'No, don't bless Daddy. You go away to work. Yes bless Daddy. You're home now. You didn't bless Granty and Howard.'

"I said 'I haven't got to the twins yet.'

" 'Bless Granty and Howard. They're only little boys aren't they? They're my baby brothers.'

" 'Bless Mummie' I said.

" 'Yes bless Mummie. She's at the hostital because she's got a sore tummie.'

" 'Amen' I said.

" 'Amen Daddy I'll go to sleep now. I won't talk. I won't get in your bed. I'll sleep all night. I won't get up in the middle of the night and come into your bed. I won't talk. I'll go to sleep.' And on she goes chatter chatter chatter . . . you should hear her chatter! She really gets wound up. And of course she does wake and come into my bed. Ever since her mother . . . Oh but she knows everything and has an opinion on everything . . . Germaine I want you to come and see the kiddie some time . . . um? Could you drop in some time? I'd love you to see the children . . . so you've bought yourself a hyacinth?"

Mon Dieu can't men be boring about their children! It's

184

one of my twenty-three commandments, about number eleven or twelve somewhere there . . . don't encourage married men to start on their children. Four hours later you'll be sorry. This hyacinth is already wilting. Of course the respectable Gordon Hood, the upright Christian, doesn't take me to lunch or anything unseemly like that. That's not done in this country . . . not in the open anyway.

I move off at a slow walk when he leaves me; down the main thoroughfare to my lesson. When I've crossed the railway line though I have to stop and look back at the Tower. Rising grandly and purely with skirts of flowers at her feet just asking for another earthquake. Like the high white vision of a man of God full of faith and fearing nothing . . . but I mustn't think like this. In no time this restless stirring dangerous second me way down underneath will get out of hand till I start neglecting my appearance. I'd start wearing my stocking seams askew and perming my hair and would end up in a cardigan for certain. And then what would happen to Style? Listen it's not you, mon cher, it's not you I'm falling for but this funny little country tucked away snugly and smugly behind its Woollen Curtain. Monsieur hates it as the devil hates holy water but I am fascinated by it: its orchards, the holiness of its sheep, the sanctity of its football deliria and racing fever, the divinity of its factory-cut clothes and morality. I think the whole thing's cute; this utter and open absorption in idols. It's the very place for people like me in spite of its import and income madness. All of which is very good thinking but don't let me wander . . . where was I.

Gordon Hood and his circumspection! He'll get circumspection if he wants it. To be candid it's what I want. Number seventeen of my commandments reads, Never give anything away to a man you mean to marry.

WHAT A STRANGE WAY to talk about yourself;
reading to us from the Scriptures! People like me tell intimate things in private if ever we tell them at all. True, you
have sat by my fire in the studio, paced in it, walked with me
in the orchards and stood with me at the lakeside beyond
but have you told me anything of you? Only the drama of
your work; your alcoholics, your delinquents, your precious
old saints in the church, your rich and your poor, your split
homes, your faithful and faithless, ever the pain in the world
and your dying. According to the rules of people like me you
should long ago have discharged your confidences. Aren't
I comely enough? Don't tell me I don't dress well enough.
Monsieur says I save his sanity, Johnnie says I'm a man's
dream come true and Gordon Hood has put in a new window
for me, a reading lamp at my bed and a shower in the

186

bathroom all for the price of one look. Whatever is wrong with you mon cher? I honestly concentrate to find out.

"Hear the word of the Lord as it is contained in the Book of Jeremiah:

" 'The word of the Lord came unto me saying, "Before I formed thee in the womb I knew thee, and before thou camest out of the womb I sanctified thee. . . ." ' "

" 'Cursed be the day on which I was born! The day when I was born let it not be blessed! Cursed be the man who brought tidings to my father saying, "A man child is born to thee." Let him hear a cry in the morning and an alarm at noon because he slew me not in the womb, so my mother would have been my grave and her womb for ever great. Why did I come forth from the womb to see toil and sorrow and spend my days in shame?'

"May God add his blessing to this reading to us of his word, and to his name be glory and praise."

But even though I sense, even know, you are speaking of yourself I still don't wholly understand. The minute everyone rises to sing "Master speak, thy servant heareth," I make my discreet escape. Brushing Gordon Hood at the door by mistake I join my fellow sinner Hugh ClanWilliam, no longer drunk unfortunately, washed, shaven, dressed in an admirable suit, but still full of irreverence and gossip, and settle down on the stone seat to hear something on a level I can follow; a most marvellous story called "What Happened at the Parsonage One Night."

"He said," I tell Léon later, "that the word of God is in his heart like a burning fire shut up in his bones and that he's weary of holding it in." I've tried not to bring up the subject.

"This priest of yours," he turns from my keyboard where he has been freeing through his fingers what has been shut up in his bones. We have arrived through music, wine, stories and coffee, all in advanced continental technique . . . at the dawn and there is only philosophy and breakfast left, "This priest of yours, with the word of God like a burning fire in his heart that he is weary of holding in. Asylums are full of artists who failed to say the things they must and famous tombs are full of those who did. I myself would have been in an asylum by now had you not released from me the chansons. A concept in the mind of a man like me, and if you like, your priest, is a foetus in the womb. There comes a time when it must be born whatever," he runs fingers through his hair, "the consequences."

He stares across the studio to where I am stretched out on the rug by the fire, trying to see me, trying to identify me, fails, and follows his thought. "A price if he does speak and a price if he doesn't; a bitter price either way. The burning word of God from a man is not likely to be applauded, even sanctioned, in a country of the Average Man; it certainly would be a matter of derision and mockery. And one does not need to live here as long as I have to find out that New Zealand actually does cultivate the suicidal cult of the Average Man; does worship the grim god of utility."

"I like this country myself. I get on with everybody from hymnbook men to drunks. I must be the Average Girl."

But of course he does not hear me. "To live in New Zealand," his eyes remote, "and preach exactly what he

188

believes must mean in the end withdrawing wholly. An honest preacher must end a hermit in this country. To the extent that an artist is truly what he believes must his life be segregated. Time after time this truth has come home to me. As one by one the people you know avoid you, and group by group they ostracise you . . . until you are faced with the ultimate decision: Do I preach or do I live?

"New Zealand is too small a country to take the real thing. I've proved it to myself. He shouldn't waste heart space, this priest of yours, in bitterness; a moment or two, a day or two would do after the latest rejection, to adjust himself to the further realisation . . . and then he should forget it. Let it fall back into the compost of the mind. Dwell on only the knowledge itself that in this country the dedicated artist cannot live. He prefers authentic reclusedom."

"I can't follow you Léon."

"It is strange to me, my heart, that you who know so well a person like me do not; that you do not understand more. How brilliance of imagery may carry an artist off into another world, a lonely and fearful world in which we are cut off from the mainstream of reality. We hear other voices speaking and see other faces; another life altogether flashes. Asylums are full of people whose brilliant imagery has carried them off forever and famous tombs are full of those who managed to get back over the border with their booty. The physical life, the bodily touch, the real fleshed union is the way back over the border. But your holy bachelor cannot do this. He can't wallow in the flesh at will. For him no plaisir clandestin, no divine opium. For him only the holy ecstasies. To my mind this preacher I so often hear ridiculed by you and the city and the press must be in both fear and pain all the time. Fear of slipping over the border and pain at not doing so. And note this my heart! It takes a foreigner to appreciate his dilemma. La chastité is his unholy sin." He reaches for his glass and finishes his absinthe and at last his visionary gaze

189

descends on me. "Where would I be without you my heart; in the asylum probably."

I uncoil myself from the hearth rug. "I can't say I appreciate the responsibility Léon. After all there are other girls in Babylon." I swing my hair back over my shoulders. "I'll make us some breakfast now . . . h'm? Some authentic coffee strongly flavoured with reclusedom. And some authentic rolls. D'know what? I'm sleepy . . ."

"I'd like to hear him for all that. What I'd like to hear him say is what he's afraid to say. I'd like to be there when he says it; this word of God shut up in his bones. If I could just time it rightly. These inspired irrationalists can be anything but boring, its only when they're afraid they're boring. That's why he's boring now."

"You overestimate him. He's only a half-inch man. You haven't heard him as I have. He's plain boring all the time in the pulpit and out. Everybody says so all the time and I always go by what everybody says. A whole lot of long sentences with far too many clauses and masses of capital letters."

"I hope your Reverend Guymer will be able to stand up to the celebrated Common Level of this country where the efficient are denigrated and the inefficient bolstered. I heard from no less than a Supreme Court Judge that the rate of suicide in this country wouldn't bear looking into."

"I heard in church once and from Doctor John more than once that . . . that a lot of famous names were bred in this country . . . and I've heard it from others too. People who have led the world in one thing or another. Split atoms and that . . . nuclear fission and beer brewing and so on . . . have you got the matches? . . . and racial integration . . . Mon Dieu I'm sleepy . . . I'm reeling sleepwards. This country can't be so bad. It's no good blaming a country just because a preacher is boring . . . listen to me defending them! Germaine defends New Zealand!" I cough my latest cough.

"These big names of yours mon coeur . . . I notice they have left these shores." Then he turns back to the keyboard and I hear the real tones of a pianoforte . . . even from this old relic! . . . as he releases what is shut up in his bones. On the open strings as well as the keys.

"Léon . . . sometimes it seems to me that you are nearer to God than the minister himself. Why don't *you* go to church?"

"Church is no place for artists."

"Why not?"

"It is now one firm class; the class of rigid respectability and appalling conformity."

"That's what he says too."

"Who?"

"The minister."

"What they can't understand, these business tycoons, this upright Dalgliesh of the three-thousand-pound drawing room, who tried to talk me into taking his daughter as a pupil . . . whom of course I refused; I require at least a percentage of native ability . . . and this fruit baron, what's his name, Hood? when he called to present the case of the church for pledged giving . . . what that kind of mentality cannot conceive is that an artist is his own church. He is in church, not each separate Sunday, but every day and night of the week. That he never ceases for a moment his liturgical and lyrical worship of truth. That he worships in his own wild way."

"He talks about his own way too."

"Who?"

"The minister."

Fingers through his hair. It's long now, cut straight about his ears like a girl and he's got quite a beard with no shaving, and more than a touch of grey in it. "I cannot conceive how he is able to endure his position in an organised middle-class church." More absinthe. "Mine is too wild a soul to be organised."

"I think that his is too."

He turns and looks out at the trees. "There is only loneliness in church for the artist."

"I think that goes for him too."

"This relationship to God they so exalt. The only relationship the artist values is the one between lovers. It's unproductive to seek any further."

"I don't think he thinks that."

"And the only lover I need is you."

If only *you* thought that . . .

You take to talking to me increasingly in the orchards I don't know why. I'm not interested in lofty talk. At my age we like things to happen all the time without stopping whereas nothing happens with you; only your coming and going and the way you go about it. Your *own* way of course. However you don't wear black clothes to me now which is possibly a happening of some kind, and which might even have meaning. You wear tweeds and a tie I might have chosen myself. Why didn't you do this before? It makes you look like a man. And none too soon either. To meet you on your own level I was about to robe as a nun. Mercifully however you've met me on mine; on the level of dress at least.

You talk increasingly about yourself these days; although only an occasional passage registers. "What's your worst trouble in your work, Mr. Guymer?"

"Vanity."

"Vanity! How can vanity survive what you get?"

"You'd wonder."

"I can't see why you shouldn't have a little regard for yourself. We're heavy on self-regard in my world. A little pride doesn't hurt anybody."

"Pride becomes a man when it is justified. 'The full-spread pride of man is calming and excellent to the soul,' but pride in myself is not justified. There's a distinction between pride and vanity; the one has reason and the other has none. My paltry little vanity has none."

We walk in silence a few steps. "What's missing in you that you can't be proud?"

You sigh just like a man. "God's word does not wholly reach me. I hear his voice but I don't know what it's saying. I know God has a definite programme for me. Before he formed me in the womb he knew me and before I came out of the womb he sanctified me. To all to whom he sends me I go and whatever he commands me I speak. I have obeyed him in not taking a wife, neither have I had sons and daughters; yet there are times, such as now, that I feel he has deceived me for I fail to divine what his purpose for me is. I do not know what he is saying. And this is my infirmity. The word of God is missing in me and I can never know pride, the full-spread pride of man, calming and excellent to the soul, when the Master does not speak."

Another day it is something just as mournful. "Why can't God's voice reach you?" I ask.

"It's the hatred in my heart."

"Not in *your* heart surely!"

"In my heart. The burden of my hatred for this country. It's an obstruction to the inner ear. I can't hear God with it there."

"But you can't hate your sick and your suffering and all the others you see."

"No. Suffering makes people real; they lurch back to their basic selves. It's not them I hate. It's the body of the people as a whole. Their ways, their words, their clothes and their lives. I hate the very air they use. I hate the way they walk, the way they talk, the way they think and what they do. I hate the way they worship and the way they profane. I have them with hate radioactive. So I do not hear my God."

"But I like this country! I even like the traffic cop who reported me to the supervisor. And you've no idea how much I like this supervisor through whom I hope to be reported to the magistrate. I'm going to be mad on the magistrate when I finally manage to be taken to court. But no one will take me to court; they just say, 'I won't be so lenient next time, Madame.' This city's a paradise for sinners."

"It's the way you sin I expect. I can quite understand that a traffic cop wouldn't know what to make of a lawbreaker with Style. It's not so much *what* you do as *how*."

"I like everyone in this country. I think they're really cute."

"You don't know what it is to be mocked and derided whenever you preach God's word. I have twenty-three personal commandments also I use outside the famous Ten called 'How to avoid slights from New Zealanders.' But I probably need sixty-three. The first is 'Never be your real self with a New Zealander.' "

"Ooh I heard something like that just the other night." Dawn if I must be accurate. "What else have you got in yours?"

"Don't ask ANYONE for ANYTHING. Abandon sincerity; let no man see your inner self . . . I can remember them I've written them all down . . . Never believe anyone when he promises to do a thing. Make no promises, believe no promises. Never speak with real seriousness to anyone. Never show your happiness or unhappiness. Never go out when you're drunk with the holy ecstasy. Never ring up, never talk when you're like that. Never speak about your work.

194

Never utter anything important to you. Never give the best of yourself in conversation. Never, never . . . NEVER! speak of your work at any time, under any circumstances, to anyone drawing breath or breathing it out . . . under pain of living agony."

I reach up and pull some new blossom; it has a marauding bee. "I don't have the one about 'Don't ask anyone to do anything for you.' You must be wrong about that Mr. Guymer. I'm always asking New Zealanders to do things for me and they keep on doing it without stopping. The only thing they won't do is take me to court."

"May you never need the commandments that I do."

It's in the late afternoon we walk amid the newly breaking blossom. I find you waiting beneath the trees when I come out from practise; which I appreciate and I find myself not less shivering with the sense of sin than warding off tenderness, my new subversive enemy and considerably more dangerous to people like me. The rays of the spring sun slant low at this time and there's vitality in the air. Late afternoon sounds are more penetrating and sweeter and birdsong more exhilarating. Shadow is deeper and light brighter making contrasts stronger. Intellects and emotions are at their best and more exciting the inner music. The distance between us is shorter and I use your name more easily. "What's worrying you today Mr. Guymer?"

"Mood."

"I haven't noticed it."

"My church knows my moods."

"You've a right to your moods haven't you? Everyone has them. I have them often myself. No doubt your Great Delus . . . sorry! . . . no doubt your God has too."

"I'm not always in the mood for preaching. A man looks

195

for inspiration in his congregation when it is missing in himself. And sometimes I receive it. There are times when I believe there is someone in my congregation who gives it whom I have not yet recognised."

"One of your holy old saints."

"No. It has come only since this influx of newcomers. Some proud sinner I feel with a native sensibility and a strength of feeling God would rather use than mine. Someone whose joy in life is undiluted by the pain in the world as mine is."

"You give too much of yourself to pain. You'll run out of giving one day. Do you ever run out of giving?"

"Often."

"And then what do you do?"

"I go to someone else and replenish myself."

"You don't go to God?"

"I find God through people."

And the things I hear about your church! If only your parishioners could hear them! "I'm not impressed by mere brute figures," you flare with your sudden belligerence as the wind is rising one day. "When I view my burgeoning membership rolls I ask, 'Is all this more than a serving of tables?' What does a full church signify; that anybody is listening?" I find no reply for the wind lifting your hair and loosening your tie makes you look more like a man of men than ever so that I feel more like a woman of men than ever; I have more trouble warding off this tenderness and this sense of uncomfortable quickening, both unfamiliar to people like me.

We reach the romantic lakeside and stand together here looking across the water at the island tomb. "Those exams," you ruminate more to yourself than to me, "are to weed out the congregation, which is overrun at the moment with

weeds. Casual careless thinkers and slow surface feelers; their
religion unreflective, uncritical, not actually touching their
living; coming nowhere near to embracing the whole mind.
It's the conditioned mind that comes to my church, ever the
conditioned mind. These people have values of a kind I
know but the self-centredness of them appalls me."

Your self-centredness, to be frank, appalls me. How can
you talk of religion standing with me on a lakeside, looking
across the water to this secluded island? There's a track
across there is there not? Any normal man would be feeling
anything but religious. But from you I get a sermon. What
waste of all my sympathy and of all this difficult thinking;
what waste of a scarlet Russian jacket and a late afternoon
mood; what waste for that matter of an island with a tomb
and drooping willows. . . . Mon Dieu, you're a stubborn
bachelor!

"Their bickerings," you continue prosaically, "are so boring. Even in the work of the church, at meetings and social
functions. It is all so irrelevant to the mature mood of aspira-
tion and wonder that should grace a major church."

"But they seem to get results, Mr. Guymer." I hope I've
said the right thing.

"RESULTS!" you suddenly roar and take to pacing the lake
edge. "This expectation of a circuit for RESULTS! Visible,
tangible, scientific RESULTS! What a dreadful thing . . .
DREADFUL!" I and the late birds move out of the way. "The
iron framework of respectability in this church! RESPECT-
ABILITY!" Boom . . . boom . . . "The SUFFOCATION of it!"

Sometimes I find myself talking a bit though not very
often. It's a habit I haven't got, talking at a man. As a role
I was born to listening. "Did you hear my sermon on Sun-
day?" Yes that's what started me off. Out comes something
I have often thought out in private and have spoken of to
Léon. "You put far too much of yourself into your preaching
Mr. Guymer. You should add that to your sixty-three

commandments. 'Don't speak with feeling to congregations.' Far more meaning would get through without all that emotion. And look what you do to the Scriptures. The word of God if it is what you say should be quite capable of getting itself over a man's tongue without all that support from you. It's what we call interception in music. Some pianists are faced with that problem though I'm not faced with it so far. They wear their music as you wear your Scriptures, like a garment Monsieur says. My music master says that a pianist should be a good transmitter and I think that you should be too. It is you rather than God who reaches us." I hold down my blowing hair. "You seduce those people you know."

You answer in gentlest reproof. "God USES personality. He created it himself in the first place. He speaks through a man's personality. Personality is not interception."

"It is in a concert hall anyway."

You smile as you always do when I'm contentious. "I still say," I continue, "that the thing between you and your congregation is no more than an human emotion and a mere emotion has its life."

You pocket your hands ruefully. "It's true that some are drawn to me and others veer away."

"With a true preacher, as with a true pianist, there should be none of this drawing and veering. Monsieur Montigny says so. He said about you, 'Methinks thou dost protest too much.'"

"'Methinks,'" you repeat voluptuously concerned with yourself, "'thou dost protest too much.'" You look idly across at the island seeing nothing of what it was created for then take to a little pacing along the wasted lakeside.

And one other time I talk. "I'm broadcasting next Sunday," you remark as we set out into the blossom, forever on the subject of yourself these days.

"Well don't waste your precious radio time roaring at us for not going to church. We all have our reasons and the decision is ours. All you've got to do is to let us see this church; give us some data to decide on. *Be,*" I exhort, "the church."

" 'Be the church,' " you repeat softly after me then suddenly glance up. "You'd make a good preacher yourself."

"May Baal preserve me from that."

We are approaching the studio from the plain one day, one very late afternoon. The sun's late rays lie prostrate and there's only one bird left. "You are the only one," you speak softly to yourself, "I am able to talk to. I can tell in your eyes you are listening. You've no idea what this means to a preacher that someone should actively respond. It makes a man endeavour. It inspires a man to the best in himself. The only one," you whisper again. "I could talk to you for hours. For hours and hours and hours."

I lift a cold hand and lay it on my cheek. You speak with growing conviction, "I could talk to you for a week."

"This wind is cold isn't it? We'd better hurry. It might even rain and this jacket cost forty guineas."

We walk the rest of the distance in silence. "Now," you say at the gate, your voice rising and your eyes turning to Babylon, "back to the routine and the mundane. The ROU-TINE!" Full stop. "And the MUNDANE!" Then you probe in my eyes for a moment, stroke my cheek in your own way and take your place in your car.

"ANYWAY!" You wrench the afternoon back to where you found it in the first place, "bless you."

It is Gordon . . . I wouldn't dare let Léon know I still see you . . . it is Gordon I tell about all your hate when I meet him beneath the Clock Tower. "He hates everybody that's what he said."

"Germaine he doesn't. Don't be upset he doesn't. He loves everybody I know this man. I'm knocking about with him most of the week. He's . . . I know a lot that you don't. He's . . . it's like being in love with someone and if she rejects you you hate her. When you're my age you'll know . . . you'll recognise love in its many disguises. Both hatred and love arise from the same source. Hatred is . . ."

"I know what you mean now. A friend of mine . . . he said that hatred is inverted love. He . . ."

"It's because his people reject him Germaine. It's the hatred of the rejected lover. You see now. One of these days you're going to hear him read from Hosea again. I've seen these swingings in him over and over again. This hatred of his is a manifestation of his love for all. Believe me and . . ."

"I can't follow all this Gordon it's too deep."

"You'll follow it when you hear him professing love again."

"You didn't hear him as I did. He . . ."

"I've heard him like that many a time. Both in and out of the pulpit. Now cheer up. I'll be out on Saturday afternoon and do you know what? D'you know what little lady? I'm bringing my little girl with me. You wait till you see my little girl! Y'know what she said last night . . ."

Doctor John says though, "He's got one of these swinging temperatures on the emotional level; as you see in a patient with some deep-seated disease. Sky-high in the evening and below norm in the morning. He could do with some sanatorium treatment." He thinks. "I'd prescribe him a damned good tranquillizer."

All of which is far too involved for people like me.

Galaxies of blossom . . . reaching breast-high from the bowl on the floor. Branches of them clustering, pink white pink in hot lustful undress filling the room with incense to Baal. . . . Outside in the orchards acres and acres of them breathing their colour upon the countryside.

Fancy preaching a sermon over the air about being in love with the world; I can barely believe it. How many do you expect to fool with this analogy of Christ? Maybe your church but not me, mon cher. Listening in seclusion at my radio without your restless presence I follow this sermon completely.

Is it possible you don't know what you're revealing to me? Or do you mean to tell me this way? Translating your earthly passion into terms of the transcendental dismays even me. It must appall the Divine Lover himself.

To awake in the night, I hear, with the name of the Beloved on your lips. This caressing of His name at dawn and in the evening twilight. To rise to the wind of the morning to a glow upon the world, not knowing at once the reason. The picture of a day waiting framed in the Almighty Beloved.

I rise from the radio to prepare for John but pause for a voluptuous time. I waken myself to find a cigarette but I'm a long time lighting it. Too long removing my clothes; too long powdering my legs. Far too dangerously long drawing on the Chinese gown and fastening its satin buttons. This indolent abandoned sloth like a shot of pethidine.

My arms change to serpents. Glistening scented screws turn in the places of the body that were formed only for men. I hold my hands on my breasts to still them; to still what will not be stilled. Is this how it is with you, mon cher?

I lie across the pink chair, breathing in the incense about me "with intoxicated, slow gluttony." I have not heard a sermon; I have drunk African wine, bitter, a liquid that burns stars in the heart.

Dream a little, you said, before answering a friend, before asking the question. Longer pauses in converse, deeper listening to each other. Longer the thought before entering a home, a hospital or the condemned cell in a gaol. Longer before burying a body, before lulling the bereaved. Ponder before marrying two in love, before baptising the newcomer; before blessing the drunkard, the weary idolater.

Let the soul stretch, you said, know itself and speak, to direct each move of the day. Let it settle, look up and purify; Blessed are the pure in heart, you said, for they shall see God.

Words, words . . . words, carrying convulsive thrills.

"But come, my heart," says Monsieur at my lesson in the city on Tuesday. "You must keep this new feeling of yours out of your exercises. With the arrival of feeling you must learn discipline. There's a time for emotion and a time for execution, and exercises require only technique. Feeling must not interfere with work. It's work that brings results not feeling. If you can't control emotion you can't control work. Emotion must be disciplined." He is always different when he's teaching; impersonal . . . austere.

I sigh and lift a hand to my face. "I've had enough of technique." We are sitting side by side formally at his piano-forte in his Town Hall studio. "I'd like to get on to the chansons."

"God knows I'm glad enough to see some feeling for music arise at last but its not time yet to indulge it. Believe me Germaine, you'll be a very fine pianist in time if you can integrate it with your technique. But that time has not yet come."

"Don't be so cruel Léon."

"How often have I heard that before in the past and from people who have become world names."

"I'm no longer keen on becoming a world name. I only want to play your chansons."

"So do I want you to play my chansons. And that's why you'll continue with exercises."

"Exercises are killing the music in me. All I want from music now is the galaxies of blossoms the chansons flash in my mind. Have mercy on me Léon. I'm tired of wanting to be famous."

"I'm not tired of wanting to be famous though. And it's

your performance of my work that will bring fame to me. I've waited for it long enough."

"What I can never make out is why you don't present them yourself. No one could play them as you do."

"The need to do so is atrophied. Besides . . . since you released my chansons I'm different. I feel more benign. This unique inspirational quality of yours . . . do other men feel it? I need no more than one as audience now and that one is you. I no longer need to return to France."

"But *you* can't stay *here*."

"Can't I? I'll tell you something that no one knows. New Zealand's national sport is not football; it's music. They don't know it that's all. New Zealanders can *see* alright but they're far too secretive to admit it. Besides it's the utter beauty of the place; the brilliant light . . . the purity of the colours. But what's the matter my heart that you should talk like this?"

"Nothing."

"There is. You've changed."

"I'm tired. I'm not well that's all. Haven't you heard my cough?"

He rises and moves off tapping his pocket for the matches and stands at the table heavily heaped with papers. It's not a very good sign.

"Have you seen anything of your priest lately?"

"Only in church."

"If only one could believe you Germaine."

"Of course I haven't seen him! I never see him at all I . . ."

"You're a poor liar, Germaine. Lies and music don't agree."

I lift my eyes and say nothing. Suddenly he strides back to me and thoroughly outraging the discipline he has been expounding plunges his fingers in my hair; they are trembling.

"Why do you love me Léon?"

"Such 'oblivion lives on your lips . . .'"

"I mean what made you love me in the first place?"

204

"You are so soft to touch . . . so soft . . ."

I push my hands against his coat. "Not here Léon, not now. It's time for music."

"It's time for love . . . my delight . . . my destiny . . ."

After this sermon on love of yours I have one of these "absolutely have to" compulsions the following Sunday to come to church. Her serene aloof steeple gazing out through the unintelligible darkness draws me as powerfully as sin. Yet when I arrive I stall, furs, coiffure and all. No wine and no Gordon spell no entry and there's only the stone seat left. So that here I am lurking at the feet of this great grey stone edifice to God no better than the Villain himself, feeling strongly *persona non grata*. You have raised him up and levelled me down so that we now meet on a common sober mean. How have the scoffers fallen.

However we are still alive and still young . . . the thunderclap has not followed our lightning yet . . . and here he is my Villain draped over the nearest stone seat in the unreal lighting and shadows and I can do with Hugh Clan-William. I find arising in me these days for this lighthearted enigma a tendresse cordiale unfamiliar to people like me. For one thing he is unmarried and can accompany me in public unlike Gordon or John or you, and for another since the metamorphosis in his appearance he is worth being seen in public with which I can hardly say of Léon. Above all he's young and I like young men. They were my only companions in Paris with the security of Raoul behind me but without Raoul they're another thing. Without a middle-aged husband it's different. I find myself these days gravitating to men a generation older as though each one were a husband, but I still prefer young people like me. Single personable romantic ridiculous and young is Hugh, considerations not to be taken lightly. Of course he seldom has money of his own but he's bound to have someone else's.

The stone seat is hard and the night is cold and I shouldn't really be here. There are all sorts of reasons for coming to church and even more reasons for not, and once I have got this far there are all sorts of reasons for going in and even more reasons for not. But the real reason why I make the effort at all remains unrevealed to me. In any case I'm not very good at reasons for or against anything. My main law of behaviour continues to be whether I absolutely have to or not . . . and tonight, after your sermon on the air, I find that I absolutely have to.

"I'm the ideal man in the eyes of maids," claims Hugh ClanWilliam.

I doubt if I could describe him. He's like the young King David in the extravagance of his manliness. No hat now and no beard and as for his clothes . . . a symphony in fawns . . . the style does credit to even fashionable Babylon. Only a small square of sticking plaster on one last knuckle records the drama of the parsonage. Waiting to meet his Purity after church he leans elegantly over the back of the old stone seat.

"I'm over six feet tall," he marvels, "ravishingly good-looking, I dress with consummate taste, I have a manner both profound and gentle, an incisive intellect, the gift of language and a propensity for conversation valuable for its flexibility. Added to all of which is a social presence which enables me to mix equally well with wharf labourers and professors; with ministers and glamour girls."

"Fancy . . . isn't it wonderful."

"Don't interrupt me Gomer . . . nevertheless I have the initiative and the courage to . . . this natural eloquence of mine should be on some kind of rostrum, a stage or a pulpit don't you think? . . . courage to contest conformity and

206

replace it with originality . . . I'm just warming up. . . . All the great were like me in youth; Tolstoy, Byron, Baudelaire, Burns . . . we just capture the imagination naturally. Yet I strive to curb any tendency to arrogance, endeavouring consistently to bring to bear an attitude of humility to all my social relationships."

I can't help laughing, although I don't really feel like it. There's a fog in the city that makes me cough and the new kind of feeling in the air breathed by the spring or the bridal orchard blossoms or your sermon on the air last Sunday or my recent illness has played the very devil with my organs.

"Now stop that Gomer, I'm serious. All this has a devastating effect. People come up to the parsonage and pour out their souls to me. From senior men regretting they've divorced their wives, through the veriest delinquents to middle-aged worried women. I seem to have a medicinal effect on them; I seem to possess an uncanny psychological insight which surprises even myself."

"Oh Villain . . . your admiration of yourself is out of control."

"Maids keep ringing me up. I find myself turning down invitations to everything from balls to barbecues with monotonous regularity. They keep on ringing me all the time without stopping. Yet they know I've got no money. They pay for the theatre and cabaret tickets and buy my petrol and oil. Got my repaired watch from the jeweller . . . three or four pounds that was . . . got my shoes repaired and they even hire my evening suits. At least five maids would marry me at once."

His voice drops to the minor. "But these maids never give me the chance to court; the most exhilarating privilege of man. They withhold from me the thing I value most in a woman; her inaccessibility. This one precious thing is denied me so that strictly my beauty is a curse."

"What about Elizabeth?"

"It was she who paid for my watch and got my shoes repaired. How I look back on those Sunday nights when she was quite unaware of my existence. I almost wish that something would happen to make it hard for me again. It's only her purity that keeps me now."

"Do you ever take her out?"

"No. I try to maintain at least the appearance of a struggle and fortunately her mother and father supply a minor struggle, since she's never apart from them. But not enough to eliminate what I see in her face when she looks up in my eyes after church." He walks to his reflection in a car window. "Did you ever," he marvels, "see eyes like mine?"

"But what about *her* eyes?"

He leans closer to his own reflection. "What exactly is the colour of my eyes would you say? Would you say aquamarine? One maid said they had the mystery of the deep deep sea. And Gomer . . . look at this profile!"

"It should be on a coin." I lean back, cross a leg and light up a cigarette. "When are you returning to Varsity? I might be going to miss you."

He takes a turn or two glancing at his own form. "I haven't made up my mind yet. It's the impossible atmosphere down there. Students are so vigorously religious these days; atheism is old hat. If they could only see that God is no more than an invention of the ego created by man in his own image; the result of the influence of parents or others or even the church itself. A throw-up from sorrow and bereavement, from fear and gratitude, from the ravages of sex turmoil or even from some genuinely mystical experience which they have misunderstood. If only they could see that religion is no more than a culturally sanctioned vent for over-strong emotions, a device to keep people out of the hands of the police and that its function is to promote social stability . . . I say what do you think of my eloquence?"

208

"Whew!"

"What do you mean whew?"

"Your eloquence!"

"I just can't help it."

"And your ardent atheism. What does the Half-Inch think of it?"

"We seldom discuss religion for which I'm devoutly thankful."

"What particular compulsion have you to use the word 'devout'?"

He is silent believe it or not.

"Surely your prolific vocabulary can supply a less religious word?"

Still the unlikely silence.

"You could have said 'profoundly thankful' or 'deeply' thankful or just simply 'thankful.' Words have overtones to people like me."

"What would you have said?"

"I'm not one of you vocab boys."

"One night when I was walking out of church I heard Mrs. Doctor John call me a snooty upper-cruster." We both roar with laughter. "I've risen in the social scale. I thought by the sermons I was a smutty lower-cruster."

"I must say that Brett does overplay the theme of original sin. Mrs. John did you say? She was the one came up to the parsonage when Brett was out and poured out her soul to me replete with anguished utterances. All about their only son. It seems that he's . . . Stan's his name . . . he's playing up at high school and has taken out his savings and bought a motorbike and haunts the jukebox joint. He's down there at this very minute. Given up church. She said his father couldn't do anything with him."

"Is all that true?"

"I promised her to go after him. Which meant changing

into Teddy Boy clothes myself and spending an evening or two down there. I learnt a lot too believe me. Brett said it was a good idea."

"Why is he playing up?"

"She didn't say but I think she knew."

"Well on behalf of his upper-crusters I'll sit his damned exam. Except that I haven't been to church. You know what I bought last Friday? A Bible and a wheelbarrow. By Baal I'll show him!"

"I'll tutor you Gomer."

"Tutored by an ardent agnostic? I'd fail man for certain!"

"See that car across there?" says Hugh. "That two-toned liner on wheels? That upholstered centipede? That cost our pillar of the church, Eliza's father, two thousand pounds. American. Six hundred pounds' worth of sales tax. Two thousand pounds' worth of incense to the idols of Possessions and Speed right in the heart of the Church. You'd wonder where God came in. If they burnt that amount of incense to love it would put me right through Varsity."

"You nauseating socialist. Your government has already taken from us capitalists more than half of what we had for your wretched Welfare State. *I* know. Isn't that enough?"

"I'm not talking about socialism. I'm talking about incense. When I reflect on the length of those cars I keep seeing Jesus trudging through the dust in sandals."

"Don't bore me. Anyway Gordon's car is longer. There it is just there. I've had a ride in it too . . . several times."

"Oh . . . have you?"

Silence.

"So that's how things are going. Love progresses, apparently."

Silence again. A long one. "What about his wife?" he asks in time. "And his children?"

I see no reason to answer.

"That was one man I thought a real Christian." Another appalled silence. Suddenly I say, "Don't you get me mixed up with morality."

He looks at me. "What are your intentions with Gordon Hood."

"Honourable. I mean to make an honest man of him. I mean to marry him of course. And he means to marry me."

"Has he said so?"

"He will when I arrange for him to say so."

"Whew . . . Gomer . . ." He sits down and thinks in his hands.

"Too bad isn't it?" I say.

He rises and moves off away from me thinking. "I'm just wondering how all this fits into his attitude to church." He turns a little. "Is nothing . . ." he stares at me . . . "safe from beauty. Is not even God immune to that face."

"Tell me why is your reverend not married?"

"He said he's married to God."

"How LIKE him to be married to God!"

"He actually does seem to give everything he's got to God. He never looks at a woman . . . other than as one of his parishioners you know. On the other hand they look at him, by the living God they do."

"Fancy an atheist saying By God. You should be saying By Baal."

This unlikely silence again. "Go on talk Brother."

Silence.

"Well about these women of his."

"H'm . . . ? Oh these women? For a start there's one

211

who listens and cries at the far door of the church every Sunday and . . ."

"No . . . not really!"

"You could see her for yourself now. She's . . ."

"Is she pretty?"

He smiles. "Not like you Gomer." He looks upon my face a moment.

"What about this Elizabeth of yours in the choir? He couldn't have her closer to the pulpit short of pulling her in. I've seen his eyes on her. Have you any competition there?"

"Paternal. He says she is the only pure thing in the city and that it is his intention to keep her that way. He has baptised her, confirmed her, watched over her and means to supervise her marriage. He claims he will preserve her from the license in Babylon. It is he who has instructed her parents never to let her out of their sight. I said to him 'That tells like a story from Hans Andersen. There'll be an Ogre along some day. Round about chapter four.' And he said 'Ogres are commonplace in Babylon. If an Ogre approaches Elizabeth I'll simply take her home to the parsonage and keep her under lock and key. In my own way of course.' "

"More and more like a tale from Andersen; if not from the Scriptures. What would Babylon say."

"They'd say a good deal in *their* own way."

"Well go on about his women."

"And then there's one up at hospital but she's very ill so that's limited to eye-work alone and there's . . ."

"Is that Mrs. Hood?"

"That's right. I say you'd better get out of this fog with that cough. And there's one in the country he mentioned once, only once, someone he calls his proud sinner. He let it slip out that . . . the impression I got from what he said was that he needed to see her regularly to . . . to keep his mental and spiritual balance in Babylon. He . . ."

"What about his emotional balance."

"Oh I don't think . . . I don't think nice ministers . . .

aa . . . talk about that." He takes one of my cigarettes. "He said something about her close natural naked way of speaking that . . ."

"Don't tell me he so far forget his holiness as to use a word like naked."

"You can take it from me Gomer that he is already emotionally betrothed to God. In his prayers he addresses him as Beloved."

"You never know he might be thinking of a woman. He might be thinking of that one in the country. I think I'll get into the car. Coming? That's the last hymn. I think he's in love with a woman. And doesn't know it or won't admit it."

He leans elegantly on my sill. "If he is and he could be nothing could come of a triangle like that. A man, a woman and God. God is certain to win."

"Don't be silly. I can't see it. A woman has it all over God when it comes to . . ."

"You're wrong Gomer you're wrong. You women you're so frightfully foolish. You chuck away your inaccessibility at once whereas . . ." he chooses his words so carefully . . . "whereas God remains the Almighty Sought-After."

"There are times Villain when I think your eloquence is wasted on atheism."

"I can move maids to tears every night of the week."

"You haven't moved me to tears yet."

"No. But that means nothing. Because you don't show it doesn't mean you haven't got feeling. As a matter of fact I'm beginning to believe you have . . . lately. In fact there are times Gomer when I think your capacity for strong feeling is being wasted on atheism."

"I haven't got any strong feeling I . . ." The doors of the church open. "It's just that words . . ."

"There's the choir coming out!"

"Words can do anything to people like me. If a man . . ."

"Here is my rationed moment for the week."

"Words might matter after all. I've been thinking some funny things lately . . . I've been even thinking that . . . of course it's mad but . . . I'm just wondering these days if . . . how much the physical touch has got to do with l'amour. I . . ." I lift a hand to my cheek. "I . . . it's not love-making at all that is . . . well I've lost my peace of mind and I've lost it through words. Words have . . . have taken away my vineyards. That half-inch . . ."

"I say meet me down at the jukebox joint later will you? Can you? Do I look all right? This is my Crisis." He peers in the car window anxiously. "Is my hair tidy? My tie straight? Shall I do up this button or leave it undone? The handkerchief matches doesn't it? Have you got something to brush my shoes? This is the latest cut in suits you know!" He draws himself up tall and turns on his profile.

"Put that hanky in a bit. Loosen the tie a little; sort of casual. Here wipe your shoes with this. Leave the button undone; avoid formality. Don't look as though you're *trying*. Now don't *rush* at her. Just appear to be passing by accident. If this is not courting then I don't know courting. Have you got something ready to *say*. What are you going to *say*?"

"I'll say 'It's not without some trepidation not to mention temerity, and a strong ingredient of humility that I . . .' "

"Mon Dieu!"

"I'll say 'Hullo, is that you, Miss Dalgliesh?' "

"Oh . . . Villain! Say . . ."

"I'll just say naturally 'It's pleasant to see you.' Will that do?"

"Why not risk sincerity? I often do in a crisis. The last-resort technique."

"All right. I'll say 'I've been waiting to see you Elizabeth.' " My hand lifts suddenly to my cheek.

"You'll have that Hand catching you if you're not careful little Gomer. What's the matter, don't you feel well?"

"Dieu! I must go! May love progress."

214

"Isn't it funny how sincerity works? I've never felt more confident in my life. I *have* been waiting to see my maid. 'I've been waiting to see you Elizabeth.' "

"Any cars coming . . . can I turn here?"

"Here she comes!"

"'I'll meet you at the jukebox after; I like young men best.'"

"Here she comes . . . here she comes!"

I all but strike an oncoming car. How would that sound in the Magistrate's Court? "I hit the car because I saw true love."

Why preach of order with disorder in the blood? Can there possibly be any order with the fruit blossom breaking? Why try to sort out the holy from the human when they're plainly part of each other? Why waste this season of spring surrounded by orchards of incense, examining obscure questions like secondhand religious sentiments and Master-Sentiments when the answers are obvious in the orchards? Even people like me can read them. This life of the trees is valid and clear and has nothing to do with morality. Waking to the spring these mornings I have the milky innocence of these trees. I am your city but not iniquitous. I am the princess of Jerusalem but my whoring from God is not terrible. I am a blossom on a branch knowing life with intimate eyes. How amoral the morality holding you! Forget, mon cher, the secondhand and Master-Sentiments, the holy versus human, immoralities and sin. Receive me graciously, speak to me tenderly, give me back my vineyards and I'll render the fruit of my lips.

How much there is I don't follow! How can your eyes speak to me in the way they do without confirming what they say? How can you preach a sermon on love yet not translate it in kisses to me? Why don't you bring me flowers to celebrate the spring between us? Why don't you visit me at ever shortening intervals instead of including me on your rounds? What an humiliation to people like me to be merely incidental!

How can I endure so laggard a lover! Why don't you convey to me in some material way the awakening between us? The most pedestrian ways would do. An armful of Gordon's wood carried in occasionally on our way in from the orchards since you all but trip over it there? Or dig a patch of garden or plant something? Why not an innocent present; some garden tool as Gordon gives me, some wine like Léon, some black nylon like John or even a book of driving rules like the lenient supervisor? Why not take me for a drive, accompany me to the theatre or invite me to visit you? Why can't you come in the evening and give the Chinese gown a chance? Is there anything so immoral, indecent or unholy in any of these questions? What's wrong in the mechanism of bachelors? At what stage is your technique? Why don't you ever *say something!*

I can't make out why you visit me only in the late afternoon and never at all in the evening. Don't I visit you at church in the evening? No doubt you have pressing engagements, I hear them in the notices. Fellowship or Trustees on Monday night, Leaders or Confirmation on Tuesday night, Bible Lectures or Temperance on Wednesday night, Quarterly Meeting or Youth Club on Thursday night . . . is this order right? Bible Class or Delinquents on Friday night, what's left for Saturday night? Farewells, Receptions, Guild, no that's wrong, Guild is about Tuesday in the afternoon, do the ladies do that? Building Committee, Teen-agers, Membership, Missionary and Marriage Classes, where do they go? Private Counselling, Hospital Visiting, how am I doing? Getting it right? Don't leave out Sermon night, about Thurs-

216

day I think when you prepare your blasts for Sunday, ooh and I left out the services at the Hospital some time on Sunday. Then of course you may be up all night with some super-thirsty alcoholic, puff, puff, where was I . . . I must not wander . . . ANYWAY! Granted you have pressing engagements in the evening but tell me, what could be more urgent than Idolatry Classes at Three Trees? Other men, just as busy, engaged in Current Affairs and Public Welfare and Private Interests find time for these classes in the evening. But you . . . you fit me most humiliatingly into your routine rounds whenever it chances to suit you. There are times, mon cher, when I feel so insignificant in the shadow of my Almighty rival that I'd give up the battle forever. This affair is written in six flats.

And another thing while we're on this subject of you, if we are ever off it. Why do our conversations continually turn on yourself and never on me or mine? Am I no more than audience material? How can a concert pianist wholly geared to the platform be audience material? What attempt do you make to see life as I do . . . the queen of your "tough visiting" list? Do you allow any views of life other than your God's? As weeks at a time go by between your discreet calls and as spring speaks in whispers of summer, my poor organs don't settle any better. I've no idea where they are at any given moment. L'amour does not progress on eye-work alone, churchly handclasps, finger tips on cheek, chaste walks in the orchards and sermons untranslated. L'amour needs its quickening confirmed. Is it true that my rival is God?

But what chance has a mere spirit against beauty like mine? Surely I defeat the Invisible! The spirit of God doesn't spend hours creaming his face and legs and washing his hair in rain water; or if he does you haven't said so. No spirit, divine or diabolic, has "la douceur qui fascine et le plaisir qui tue," has hair as black and eyes as blue. How can any spirit, of God or of Mammon, touch the senses of a man, married or bachelored, with the precision of a practised woman? I can't see that God has a chance.

What waste of admirable technique in a pulpit! Is it never to be translated? Does it begin and end in a pulpit or is it a matter of the highest bidder? Do you mean, mon cher, to bring me pain instead of the joy Christianity professes? Are all these unsolved questions going to wreck my practise, cancel my appointments on the continent and kill my concert career? Is this stuff of heaven and hell banking up between us doomed to die in shivering morality so that I end up in craven repentance?

Christ! can't you wake up and *do something!*

We are walking through these orchards one day; you are taller than me and your step is longer. So is your thought taller than mine and your vision longer. Yet here you are including me on your rounds, carrying out your pastoral duty. It is hard for me to believe, if not totally impossible, that it was you, walking slowly with me through these orchards, prosaic in tweeds, who preached that sermon on love.

For one thing you are still expounding on the dreary subject of your work and all the difficult people in it; still grieving over your city like a rejected lover; trying to divine if her heart breeds some dark flame behind the incense in her eyes; this voluptuous giantess of yours sprawling carelessly across the countryside conceiving each night her gargantuan children. You are still elaborating on her erring ways and her whoredom from under her God; selling the righteous for silver and the poor for a pair of shoes, turning aside the way

218

of the meek, forgetting the brotherly covenant, despising the law of the Lord and profaning his holy name. And for another your presence is so human: how can a man with hair lifting in the under-tree draughts, with lined and roughened skin, a collar and tie like other people and tweeds with warp and woof be involved with the transcendental? You'd be more in character cultivating the ground beneath these trees with a rotary hoe like the labourer we hear plainly at this moment in the orchard adjoining. You outrageous complexity of holy and human!

Nevertheless as we walk together amid the massing turbulent blossom, the smell of the damp soil, the droning of the engine in the distance and with the birds chanting the ecstacies of both spirit and senses, more and more I think I'm your City. It's I who burns incense to idols. Who is it but I who squanders an inheritance on fashion, wallows in wine and risks life in speed? It's I who commits adulteries plain and fancy to leave the fatherless without mercy; who offers pleasing odours to images, the work of my own hands. It's I whose lies cause me to err, who casts off all pity and whose anger against God tears perpetually. It is I, the transgressor, who takes the greatest care of my body with no thought for the care of my soul; I, the terrible princess of Jerusalem defiled by Baal. Indeed and indeed as we walk together through the charged coloured incense of this both holy and lustful temple of nature and as tree by tree my depravities add up and as the feverish beauty of the blossom speaks to me with its urgent physical directness I feel myself to be so much the authentic Madame City that, forgetting the sinlessness of my spring mornings and remembering only the meaning in your sermon on love, I absolutely have to *do something* myself. Surely it cannot be beyond the technique of people like me to usurp in your heart the worship due to the divine.

We are both within the studio dripping and puffing, your heavy breathing more mortal than ever. "H'm," is your only comment. Flash of lightning . . . crack of thunder, nearer. I hold my hands over my ears.

"Dry your things on this chair here sir. Put some of this radiogram on the fire a friend smashed up. I never know where these violent storms come from. Have you got a name for this sort of thing?" This is the temple of Baal, the temple of Baal, the temple of Baal. "Or is this hydrogen-bomb weather?"

"This is a special from the Pacific; a tornado." You stroll to Gordon's new window, your back discreetly turned. "Among other specials from the Pacific; such as fall-out from the tests this year and our dose of Strontium Ninety. I prefer the tornados myself." You continue talking while I change my wet clothes. In spite of the factory coat the scarlet jacket is ruined, owing to *your* own way. Its fate is the jumble-stall. "Yes," I hear, "I prefer a humane tornado myself. They come but at least they go and their destructiveness is not the will of mere man." I put on the Chinese gown and the wonderful slippers from Hong Kong . . . the temple-of-Baal-the-temple-of-Baal-the . . . and let down all my hair to dry, strictly to dry.

"Is all this frightful noise necessary I wonder? I'm allergic to frightful noise. Isn't it dark in here!" I switch on the light; no light. "The power is off. The kettle will have to go on the flame."

A flash of lightning like youth; everything momentarily shows up; the mats on the bare floor and the nailheads even, the wall-length wardrobe, the reading lamp over my pillows, my wonderful piano lying open and my wonderful bed lying shut, the tulip on the table and the wine. The shape of the past flares up, the lightning of the present and the following unknown of the future. Then all is destroyed in the thunder.

When it is over I take my hands from my ears and put the kettle on the flame, a little flame with a future; then I take a crystal glass and fill it with Léon's wine and drink it. This-is-the-temple-of-Baal—where man keeps the keys of pleasure but you don't use these keys like other men so I fill the glass again and drink it . . . the-temple-of-Baal-the . . . But you don't feel wine at once just as you don't feel sin at once so I fill it again and lift it and look through its sparkling redness. A little higher and follow it with my eyes. "A l'idole immortelle," and drink it. Now maybe I'll feel better. "Come and dry yourself by the fire, Mr. Guymer. Sit in this old pink chair." You pick up the bottle in passing and examine the label before you sit down. I get out the silver teapot centuries old, and the china cups I brought out with me, very pure white a single black tulip on each. Is there any milk I wonder? Let me see do you take sugar now . . . ooh, and the tea tin; you Néo-Zélandais and your tea. All this done before the wine catches up and before White Furnace within catches up . . . Some time in silence while the water comes to the boil and the wine too, then I make it and pour your tea and a petal from the real red tulip falls in upon it and floats there and I leave it there as I pass it.

Your drinking is quiet so maybe your eating is too. How do I get this sense of casual origin? From your furtive pressure of my hand one night at the door? I still suspect you are the kind of man who would kick his toe on the bed as you came round and curse at the very wrong moment, take all the bedclothes with you when you heave over at night and I cannot imagine you carrying me home gracefully over your shoulder after a party; I'm still nervous of crude technique . . . I brush my eyes anxiously; "I beg your pardon? What were you saying?"

"I was inquiring after the manner of your life before you came to Three Trees."

I settle down on the rug before you only to dry my hair . . . and cough interestingly. "I must dry this hair. Not that the rain ever hurts it."

"Where and how did you live, Mrs. Jones?"

"Is that important for you to know?"

You think with concentration, watching the petal on the top of your tea. "Yes," you reply with care.

"You weighed that word," accuses the wine.

You look up innocently, then smile.

"Yes you did. You weighed that word, I saw you."

Your smile widens. "And you're still weighing your answer."

"I see no reason to answer everything. It's a habit we could well grow out of."

"You still haven't answered, I notice."

"It's far too direct to answer. Cultivated dalliance is oblique and I'm disposed to dally at this hour. If only you Christians," warms up the second glass, "were not so orderly, wanting questions answered all the time without stopping, and so heavily sincere, weighing your words . . . and everything. You deliberately nurture these qualities. 'I myself have seen it!' said the Lord."

"One must not blame everything exclusively on Christianity; others are involved too. But you still haven't answered my question."

"People like me can't possibly sir. You've admitted it's important to you. We avoid the important at all costs." The third glass stretches prostrate on the rug, its arms behind its head. The blue gown was created for this sort of thing. Heat within and heat without; church was never like this.

"What is your real name Mrs. Jones?"

"Is there anything wrong with Jones?"

"There's a good deal wrong with Jones. 'From the sole of the foot even to the head, there is no soundness in it.'"

"Well that's what it is sir; Jones."

"You don't put much store on plausibility do you?"

"Plausibility never brought me a sou." My inner organs respond to warmth and wine; they tentatively get up out of their hideouts and move stealthily about my body seeking their original places, pacified and less alarmed. So does inner music respond to warmth and wine. White Furnace takes to beating in that crescendo way that threatens to take me over. It does take me over I think. A flood of music spills over the barriers and drowns my efforts at thinking I don't know how long how long . . . I brush it all fiercely away . . . "What did you say? So sorry." I find you examining me, concentrating from above.

"I was asking you if you might be a celebrity or if you had occasion to avoid someone. Or . . . or do you hide from something else?"

"That's it! I'm hiding from the law! I committed a crime and I'm hiding from the law."

"I don't believe you Madame City."

"Truth is a bore Man of God."

You watch me fully for some time openly and without apology, your brown eyes steadily upon me while your cup with the black tulip on the outside and the red petal floating on the inside poises in mid-air. I stir uneasily and rise to an elbow. "You're weighing too many words," I say.

"I'm weighing you."

"I'm tired of being weighed Mr. Guymer."

"Do you know what I'm weighing OF you?"

"All my black sins I suppose."

"Do you want to know?"

"Yes please."

"I'm weighing your youth." You lean back and sip from your cup. "I'm wondering how long after the flash of lightning will follow the crash of thunder."

"Don't talk like that! I'm afraid of thunder."

"I want you to promise me something."

223

"Promises are out of date."

"I want you to promise that if you ever need me you will come to the parsonage to see me."

"I never need anyone at all."

"Do you not love anyone?"

"I love no one."

"H'm . . . won't you tell me about yourself . . . right now? You are . . . ARE! . . . after all one of my people, whether you take it seriously or not. I'm not the minister of your church for nothing."

"You make me feel doomed when you talk like that. You make me feel sinful. I'm no more than a petal fallen from a fruit tree, floating by on . . . on drifting water. Fruit trees know no sin. Nothing happens to a petal, even in a cup."

"Will you promise me?"

"I'd rather you asked me to visit you some time when I didn't need you. At a time like the Blossom Parade."

"Come to me any time; in your heavens or your hells."

"I don't have heavens or hells."

"You'd be safe in heaven or hell; it's when you're in neither you're lost."

I sit upright restlessly. "Can I pour you some more tea sir?"

"Don't get up. I'll fill it myself thank you. The second cup is always an improvement."

"The first, I take it, is rehearsal."

You reach and pour more strong tea, milk and all, leaving the petal floating. I like seeing your arm reaching, the shirt sleeve pulled into folds, and I hear the faint sound of movement. It all makes you real and human; so sought after a thing by people like me. I watch you lean back again, cross one leg upon the other and note the careful gentleness of your voice. "These values of people like you, I must confess, arise from an area of sentiment with which I am not wholly acquainted."

224

"What does all that mean?"

"It means that I can't fathom why you don't tell me about yourself."

"It's just that I'm no good at answering questions."

"No. You're very much better at asking them." Stab of lightning and a close blow of thunder and rain like Rachel weeping. I hold my ears.

"This noise upsets me dreadfully. I'll tell you that much about me. I can't stand ugly excruciating noise. If ever I do come to you in hell it will be to ask you which vein in a wrist to open to escape loud noise."

"It's the radial artery." You show me on your own wrist.

"That one there? The one showing?"

"I've seen that done before." Lightning again and the thunder and I press my ears again. You say calmly, "This is nothing to what it will be like on Annihilation Day, when the warheads are released."

"Don't talk about those things! That's one of the reasons I came to New Zealand."

"There is little else to talk of at the moment that is not meaningless, with the world itself wondering which vein." You rise in unease and stand. "Do you know . . . or care . . . that the ballistic weapons now being mounted carry nuclear warheads double the power of the Bikini bomb?" You set off on some very bad pacing. I hear as you pace all about similar weapons airborne night and day by both American and Russian commands. I hear about international agreement being a blind alley until you collide with the corner of Steinway. "It's the inspired gesture we want!" Your voice is at full pulpit level. "Only the inspired gesture can summon us out of the rigid attitudes we are all now frozen in!" I hear a good half-hour of this but you are speaking as the Church with the personal note gone and the Church when it speaks always bores me. It's time for another wine.

"No doubt," speaks up the fourth glass, "there are good

225

answers to thunderous questions like these sir but I'm short of wit at the moment."

"I doubt, Madame City, if you are EVER short of ANYTHING at ANY given moment!"

"I'm VERY short of WINE at THIS given moment! Be so kind as to pour me some. Don't spill TOO much; leave SOME in the glass. Wine is EXPENSIVE you know. Don't capital letters ACCUMULATE! Oh thank you so MUCH Mr. Guymer. There are times when I think you're WONDERFUL!"

Down comes the garment of serenity and you return relieved to your chair. "Do you really think so?" The innocent childish gaze.

"I could if others let me. But do smoke sir. This is the temple of Baal. Would you roll me one too? I'm quite out of action down here."

You take a long time over this rolling; a long pondering time. "A man must have a vent," you remark at last. "A place where he can say anything. And I seem to find it in you."

"But this is the temple of Baal, the temple of Baal, the temple of Baal, where Depravity keeps the keys."

"I still find this vent in you. A passage for the word of God." You rub your face in that way I know. "I must hear his word soon. The pressure is insupportable. I pray nightly for release and almost every waking moment."

"Someone told me recently when speaking of you that asylums are full of people who could not say what they must and that famous tombs are full of those who did. Are you either of those Mr. Guymer?"

You smile reluctantly, then broadly.

"You shouldn't smile, you should groan. You often smile in the wrong place." You lean back, open your mouth and laugh out like anything. "That's good all right. Yes that's good all right."

"I'm not a bit amused myself. What I can't see sir, is

226

where all these crises of pressures and releases come into the life of a . . . now here's a hard word to say . . . as-s-cetic, no. Try another. S-s-celibate. Too many esses there too. There's a flaw in my English for some reason; I might have to move into French. Anyway! Where was I? It occurs to me that you have these crises because you are a sh-ss . . . bachelor. Am I being too crude or shall I move into French? Je crois que la chastité est physiologique, détestable. Elle est mère de tristesse et de gastralgie."

"I'm not an ascetic. My relationship to God is anything but ascetic; it's the most sensual thing in my being. Men marry whom they need. I marry God 'morning by morning, day by day, night by night, and every marriage' is newer."

"I'm not impressed with your celestial relationship sir." I rise to an elbow, not easily. "There's a flaw in it all somewhere."

"The flaw is that I find God only through people; I find him through people like you."

"People like me hardly appreciate the honour."

"But you're so close to God."

"I wouldn't so flatter God. If anywhere at all he is close to me; I'm not interested myself. If it's true that he is attracted to me is there anything new in that? So is the traffic supervisor. Maybe it is because I do not despise l'amour on a mortal level. People like you . . . just as a spot diagnosis . . . should study first l'amour physiologique; the mechanism of it I mean. Technique is a word with more coverage. Where was I . . . don't let me wander. Maybe you do not hear what your Almighty Seducer is saying because you have not studied this preliminary technique. No one disputes that you preach ably to us on the holiness of the Master-Sentiment but what you need is some ribald rationalist to preach to you on the lowliness of the master-technique. Oo-ooh . . . 'de perdre au fond d'un lit l'antique conscience'; 'deux beaux seins, radieux' and so on, 'bras . . . des boas luisants' and

'tes jambes . . . tourmentent les désirs obscurs et les aga-
cent.' What I am trying to explain sir in my own way and
language is that saints must be sinners first. How would that
sound from a pulpit or in a Magistrate's Court? Saints must
be sinners first. I question whether bachelordom is morally
defensible. May Baal add his blessing to this astonishingly
explicit exposition of his word, and to his name be glory and
praise." I sink back prostrate again.

Look at the lightning! Listen to the rain and now the
thunder! You have to wait before you speak. Now what are
you going to say? "It would be unjust to condemn any woman
to a marriage that must take second place; for marriage is
incompatible with the life I was called to. Before God formed
me in the womb he knew me and before I came out of the
womb he sanctified me. Any love of mine that turned aside
from him would be a deviation from his plan."

"Why complicate life with marriage? God wouldn't mind
you loving a woman just for herself."

"To love a woman for herself would be signing an open
check on the bank of hell. The word of God is sharper than
any two-edged sword piercing asunder the soul. It is per-
missable to love in a woman, to me anyway . . . TO ME
ANYWAY! . . . no more than the beauty of God."

"There goes the church speaking again! That's not you!
What do you want to bring the church to my idolatry classes
for. I go to such trouble to prepare them."

You lean forward over me so that I see the pores of your
skin, its texture and lines, the too-low hair on your forehead
and the blurred brown of your eyes and I hear the movement
of the clothes on your body and the controlled breath and
know the alluring man odour. You whisper "You are closer
to God than I am."

"I'd rather be closer to Man." The tumult the turmoil
the turbulence outside and the thrashing instruments of rain.
I hear you, "Do you know what He wants me to do? Do you
. . . Madame City . . ."

"Mon cher savant . . . I know only what *I* want you to do." My eyes reach their blue tongues upward into yours and talk to you there explaining what I want you to do. They explain in profound and voluptuous detail what I want you to do. Spring lightning . . . White Furnace . . . Spring thunder.

But you lurch to your feet, the chair grating, stand a moment then swing into your furious pacing. Over to the new window, over to the old window, past the bed, past Steinway then over the whole route again. Sometimes I hear you whispering to yourself, or to your God maybe, " 'Cursed be the day on which I was born! The day when I was born let it not be blessed!' Why did I come forth from the womb to endure this travail! Abide with me, O Lord, and deliver me!" Tramp, tramp, tramp echo the holy steps through the temple of Baal. Tramp, tramp, tramp echoes Christian morality through my idolatrous mind until you return to a standstill above me and look disastrously down; until the Church recedes and Man speaks. "This child shocks me . . . this child shocks me . . ."

"Shock you? Wait till I *try* to shock you!"

The lightning again and I see you change. Down comes the garment of serenity, the trained overlay of tranquillity. From my back on the rug I see you turn, reach for the silver teapot, pour yourself a third cup, lean forward across me and my satin and my Strontium for the kettle on the hob so that I hear your abating breath, add more water to the cup, then lean over me a second time to replace it. I see you return to your chair, remove the red petal from the cup and drink this controlled tea appreciatively while clumsily rumbles the thunder.

I whisper. "If I could meet your Great Invisible sir, if I could only get within arm's length of him, I would plunge an invisible knife right through his invisible heart."

The special from the Pacific is abating too. There is still distressed rain and much acrimonious dripping but the lightning and the thunder have spent themselves. You roll a re-covering cigarette and light up, taking endless time over it. Then you smoke this cigarette, taking eternity over it. At length you rise and reach for your pullover. "Do you know what I'm thinking of, Madame City?"

"No."

"Shall I tell you?"

"No."

"You." You put on your pullover again and then the pro-saic tweed coat.

"Do you know what I'm thinking ABOUT you?"

"No."

"Would you like to know?"

"No."

"That you've not yet answered my questions." Smile.

You stoop and lay your fingers on my cheek in your own and old way so that I hear your ordered breath. "We spend our lives burning incense to idols when we could be burning incense to love. ANYWAY!" The word jerks the idolatry class in the temple of Baal to a close and reinstates the afternoon on its feet, "bless you."

Ange plein de gaieté, connaissez-vous l'angoisse . . . ?

THE APPLE TREES in the wide apple orchard across the road are not in leaf yet and still no sign of blossoms, still their empty reaching arms. Somebody said their leaves come first. The white plum nearby are whitening up more though and should soon be full by the look of them and the vivid pink of the peach and nectarine are beginning to show up through the poplar breakwinds, millions and millions of glamorous pink pearls, through the gaps in the miles of tree guards. But the old Christmas plum behind the studio is in full white blast an enchanting sight making me believe in magic . . . cascading cascading like cadenzas.

On the way to town lemons and oranges in their different yellows blare scherzando from within private gateways; I see them yellowing away into the distance in regiments. But you should see the flowers in the city: at the feet of the

Clock Tower big hyacinths blue, deep pink and white, iceland poppies and freesias. Along the railway line they've got cinerarias in bud and tulips in bud and a border of grape hyacinths in full bloom, blue, mauve and white and in the gardens round your church I see as I pass all these Brompton stock and what do you call those little gold things again now . . . I've forgotten. Your lilac and hydrangea are only in leaf bud though and the delphinium just above the ground . . . there's a lot to come yet. The willows everywhere in the flat parks are still bare and the oaks in the avenue too, they're not leaving yet neither is the poinsettia . . . ooh I know portulaca! That's the name of those little gold things everywhere in the front gardens of houses parading the paths. There's a good bit more to come yet . . . spring has a lot more to say.

I find myself standing and looking at all these, stopping and standing, getting out of the car and standing, sometimes feet astride, my hands in my pockets or arms akimbo, weight on one leg, before the flower-shop windows too . . . immobilised.

Immobilised . . .

Sometimes I say in the morning, I can't practise today and then I see a big hole full of hours I don't know what to do with, frightening hours swelling and contracting alive so that I do go and practise after all. Then at noon I say, but I won't practise this afternoon, then I see these hours again, a big afternoon hole full of them looking at me and threatening me, a widening hole with no sides so I run and fill it up with music, heap it high with music. At the end of the afternoon though when I have come in from my walk in the orchards I stop trying to fill them up and sit in the pink chair where I can see the coming blossom through the window and surrender to this immense immobility, my elbow on the arm rest and my chin in my hand. Hours now of stillness as the air becomes colder and the light gives way to dark, trying to think for a while then giving up before the inner music, surrendering to it as to a man; giving it what it wants in the way it wants. This strange new state so unfamiliar to people like me, and that I do not want disturbed, that I don't want anyone to break so that I fail to turn on the light, and steps that I hear coming they go again, I don't know whose . . . they think I am not at home. Only the steps coming and departing, the voices of the late birds and my father's clock ticking, until one evening I stir at a rising wind and get up and play all the chansons. Now I lie on my grand bed with a hand over my eyes and go on thinking of you. Not as you are now of course but as I would wish you to be.

"Gomer you masterpiece of Nature!"

"The supersonic line."

Here I am with Hugh down at his precious joint. If you want Hugh these evenings it's all his delinquents too, most of them on probation. He himself is in stovepipe and cravat, hair pulled down over his forehead. "All technique," he says.

"Move your feet over Hugh, give me some room. You're spoiling the suède of my shoes."

"Kiss me right," demands the jukebox, "kiss me wrong . . ."

"How is it I see clothes on you I never see anywhere else?"

"Style is one of my idols."

"That frock follows the contour of that body of yours with the obsession of a lover's fingers. Practically no strain on the imagination whatever."

The jukebox . . . the crowding intruding voices . . .

"I say Gomer what actually happens when men are alone with a girl like you?"

"Ooh you talk like a juvenile."

Laugh then pause. "Y'know what Gomer? You've got some terrific love affair on the go. I can tell. I'm in love myself. I know all the symptoms. Lovers can't conceal their passion. We betray our own secret."

The noise . . . too much . . . too loud . . .

"I can see it's got to the stage nice people don't talk about."

I stir my coffee for nothing, it's got no sugar in it.

"Don't tell me you're *still* in love with that exile."

"Don't make me sick."

"Gordon Hood . . . no? Doctor John . . . no? The supervisor . . . the Hungarian designer . . . no? Who else . . . the importer with imagination? None of those apparently. But I'd say you'd got to the black lace stage."

"Only the black mood stage."

"What's the hold-up . . . tell me?"

"A rival."

"There's no such thing as a rival for you."

"That's what you think."

"No one human, flesh and blood, could ever rival you."

"That's just it."

"What's just it?"

"My rival isn't human."

"Now hold on, don't explain. I'll sort this out myself. I'll just cruise off a moment while my subconscious works it out. I mean to organise a string band among these kids. I'll get at them through their hot places. Excuse me . . . sorry! Was that your foot?"

"I've got to admit I don't follow about the rival who isn't human. Music . . . or something like that?"

"Who's that boy you've been talking to, the one with the fluorescent socks."

"The King of the Baddies, the Johns' only son."

"I thought I knew that face."

"He's our latest and liveliest member. Strife in the home."

236

"Strife in Johnnie's home?"

"Stan has just been telling me about it."

"But Johnnie adores his wife."

"So . . . well there you have it. He says his mother and father haven't been getting on for weeks . . . and he can't stand it. He loves them both and can't stand it. That boy's left school you know and he was in the University entrance form. Brett thinks it's another woman. She'd let Doctor go if she knew what she was doing. It's the talk of church circles . . . I wish I could find her. I can't believe in such depravity."

"Ooh change this subject its boring."

"Have you touched your maid yet after church?"

"No."

"Haven't you even brushed each other by mistake in passing?"

"No."

"Don't you even try to now?"

"No."

"You're heavy on the 'No' aren't you?"

"Yes."

"Go on say something. Talk man!"

"It's not that I don't want to touch her. I want to . . . it's because I want to preserve her inaccessibility. After what I experience among maids imagine what this means to me. Without that I'll never marry." He strokes his hair at the back. "Mr. and Mrs. Dalgliesh have not even asked me home yet. They're aa . . . they know all about my tomcatting . . . or think they do. And I want them to know about it. See? They play my game for me. They keep her from me, that's just what I want. I mightn't be able to do it myself." His voice drops theatrically, "I do not mean to touch that maid until we have been united in holy matrimony at the holy altar, until we have exchanged holy vows and signed the

holy register. Not a finger, not a hair, not the hem of a frock.
I managed to rise from the Pit without it."

"And what will happen in the holy vestry when you've
lifted the holy veil from her face after all this holy continence?"

"I brush one light kiss on her cheek."

"You superman."

"There'll be no question of what happens to my soul when
the kissing has to stop because for me it never will."

"Oooh be realistic."

"What do you mean realistic?"

"I mean . . . I mean any kissing I start, it stops in its
midsummer. I don't like the elegaic part."

"Where will you be next year . . . round about midsummer? I may be needing you."

"Back to Varsity. Then into the ministry. Then I'll celebrate my nuptials with Elizabeth Dalgliesh."

"*You* a minister!"

"Me."

"But you were preaching atheism the last time I saw you."

"My liaison with atheism is over."

"You . . . heretic!"

"I'm all they're waiting for Gomer can't you see that? I
could straighten up this planet in a matter of weeks. I'd soon
knock their H-bombs. I've all the qualities required to sway
the mind of man. Brilliant imagery, rare looks and a surplus
of scintillating wit. I could preach with fire eloquence insight
and a touch of radiant madness. I'm the inspired irrationalist
who is going to save this world. From me will come the gesture the whole of history awaits. It will be I who summon the
nations out of their rigid attitudes of fear distrust and obsession. It's no good laughing Gomer. Surely you can see for
yourself that I'm . . . this is no time for laughing Gomer
. . . that I'm a born prophet. Just listen to me. You never

238

hear anything like this. Reason won't save us from atomic death. Reason must give way to revelation. I'm the golden prophet to interpret God's word. I guarantee Isaiah himself didn't have what I've got, he'd never have been sawn in half."

"And what's going to happen to the word of the Lord with a profile like yours in the pulpit, aquamarine eyes and such?"

"The Lord could do with my face and wit; he's been short of a face and some wit."

"Romeo if you mean to preach you'll have to get rid of those looks. No word of any Lord could possibly get past them."

"Don't call me Romeo, it's too obvious."

"But anyway . . . all that is going to make it too long to wait for your maid. L'amour is progressive I remind you. If there's one thing it hates it is . . ." I take out a cigarette . . . "it is waiting."

"Real love is excellent at waiting. Love should be postponed. Love is far too precious *not* to postpone. As long as the beloved is inaccessible it remains inspiration. And I'm going to need the inspiration. I'll touch my maid only when I'm the Reverend ClanWilliam with eighteen letters after my name. I might even do medicine too. The complete all-round healer. Science and Revelation may marry in me."

I stretch and change the position of my cramped legs under the small table. "I must go. I can't stand this noise. That jukebox . . ."

He strokes his face like you. "You know what made me drink Gomer? I knew I was called to preach and I was afraid. The fear was . . . crippling. I tried to drink myself out of it. I tried to prove I was far too sinful. A hundred times I thought of opening an artery but . . . but I still loved life too much. This ridiculous weakness about life . . . it's the most disastrous of our inclinations. What could be sillier than wanting to go on bearing a burden that should be thrown to the ground? But I learnt a lot in that pit. I learnt more than I would have above ground. 'Sin achieves a more profound depth in its ugliness than sanctity in its pleasantness.' But living all those weeks in the pocket of that half-inch man at the parsonage, sharing all he did, following him wherever he went, thinking along in company with him and praying whenever he did the idea of the ministry became normal. Not even a privilege, just normal. I came to learn how to let the soul find its equilibrium on the lower levels before I ever *did* anything. I climbed up out of the pit."

"There's too much noise in here . . . such a hard kind . . . edges . . . I must go Hugh . . ."

"I knew you weren't listening."

"Yes I was. What were you saying?"

"I'm not going to repeat all that."

"Where are those matches I saw you with . . . oh is that little gold lighter fixed? I suppose you know . . . did you know old Gordon is off down south shortly? More responsibilities for me. On top of the ones Brett hands out. He's going to open a new branch down there to save his capital from taxation he said. And he wants to take the children down to his mother's place. Have you seen his little girl? Of all the little . . . ! These beautiful brown eyes the way they look up . . . have you heard her talk? She loves me you know. It's all dreadfully sad about her mother. Brett said she doesn't . . . are you listening?"

"Um."

"He said she needn't die at all. He said she was on the mend. Doctor John himself admitted it. Brett said she fought wonderfully. She had so much to live for. But Brett said some-

240

thing suddenly broke her heart and now she's back on the transfusions. He said her heart suddenly closed to hope and said that youth must have hope. He said without hope youth's only answer to grief is death. He said he thinks it is another woman. He said he's seen it often enough to recognise the signs. I'd like to find that woman too. Ripping up a home to enlarge her border . . . these women rampant. Pregnant too, Mrs. Hood. She should never have been allowed home from the hospital that time, fools men are. Isn't . . . aren't some things worth a little continence? If I could only put my finger on that woman . . . I'd more than point it at her. A lot of this goes on in Babylon. I can't believe in such sin . . . I mean if she knew what she was doing. But Mrs. Hood won't talk not even to Brett. All this makes me think."

"Why don't women look after themselves! *I* do!"

"But . . ."

"They ask for it! They deserve what they get!"

"I don't quite . . . what do you . . . ?"

"They neglect themselves. That's a woman's first sin . . . neglecting herself."

"There must be more to marriage than that. There's many a . . . I've seen many an idyllic marriage in town with the ugliest women imaginable. You can feel it when you enter a house."

"You wait and see!"

"You're so easily upset these days I can't make it out. Have you not got over that flu? Someone should be looking after you. I'd like to see you marry again Gomer. Some large kind considerate . . ."

"I'll marry again in my own good time and in my own good way believe me!"

He leans his elbows forward on the table between us and looks at me . . . examines me in your old way. "What are you in such a rage for?"

"I'm not in a rage!" Slam goes my cup.

241

"Its an improvement I think." He lays a hand on mine. "I do believe you are developing the capacity to feel. I don't know whether to rejoice or not." He examines me longer thoughtfully. "What did you mean, your rival isn't human."

"How would you like to have God for a rival!"

"I want to go," moans the jukebox, "on a honeymoon with nobody else but yoo-oo . . ."

"I see it all."

"Kiss me right, kiss me wrong . . . !"

"For Christ's sake take off that record!"

"I see it all . . . Brett's 'proud sinner,'" He strokes the back of his hair and thinks to himself for some time. Then he speaks, his wide ocean eyes gazing beyond his delinquents to the open street. "You sin with such an air Germaine that it takes on the appearance of virtue."

I AM STANDING with Gordon beneath the three big trees; it is Saturday afternoon. He is in his dungarees and sweat and whiskers and I in the scherzo skirt; a mass of futuristic pink blossoms with black daggers through them. I have come to know socially through Léon an importer with imagination and an Hungarian refugee designer with more. The peasant blouse though I brought out with me.

There is considerably more order in the garden now, one patch dug and some unmistakable shoots.

"I know I should have waited longer, until afterwards," Gordon is saying, "before I spoke but I was afraid I might lose you. It's not just for myself I want you Germaine; it's for the children as well. I want them to be brought up near a person like you. You'll never have to do anything for them;

there'll always be a nurse in the house. I'd never let you touch a thing with those lovely clever hands. I'll give you a large studio away from the house where you can keep your piano. You may live your life just as before: practise your days away and keep your appointments on the Continent. I'll spend my life caring for you Germaine, seeing to all the things you never think about; wood and stoves and electric light. I'll build you a new house on the hill overlooking the vineyards and orchards. I'll keep a lovely garden of flowers. Nothing gives me greater joy than to do things for you; anything, anything at all. I'll beat off the reporters and keep your name out of the papers if I've got to buy them out to do it. You'll have plenty of money; you can spend what you like on clothes. I want to keep you just as you are; that's my aim. Never to go down-at-heel and fat like so many married women. To keep you exactly as you are. The blue of heaven was never like your eyes; there's not a flower in the orchards that can equal your face; not a petal as soft as your hands. No dark night was as soft and black as your hair . . . I've never dreamt of such beauty.

"I want my children to know what beauty is; to live near it day by day. I want them to know what real womanhood is and to know what music is. It's the greatest thing I can do for my babies when they lose their own mother. They're used to someone young; so am I used to someone young. I want to replace her with someone young. I must plan for them carefully and choose for them carefully and buy or fight for the best for them. They're so dependent . . . so trusting . . ."

"Don't cry Gordon; this is a happy occasion."

"All we want is to be near to you."

"Is it."

"Will you marry me Germaine."

"Yes I'll marry you Gordon."

"Oh no . . . it can't be true!"

244

"It's true; I mean it. I always have."

"But I'm so unworthy of you!"

"That doesn't matter."

"It can't be true; I can't imagine such . . . such . . . !"

"I can."

"I didn't think you would on account of the babies."

"I don't mind babies . . . ready-made."

"All this is too wonderful to . . . to believe. I can't believe it, I . . ."

"Aren't those twin boys cute. I never saw such knees. I had no idea babies were amusing. Those little white necks at the back with the curls on them; it does something to me, somehow. Two exactly the same with tipped-up eyebrows and those almond eyes and those golden curls . . . fascinating! And the two of them laughing all the time. Are they like their mother? They're not like you. And that little girl's got looks . . . how does she come to be dark? . . . She's a pretty little thing even though she looks like you."

"They do say she's like me but I don't know how she comes to be pretty. Bad luck though the boys got the curls and she didn't."

"My hair never curled and you seem to like it."

"Whatever your hair did I'd like it . . . I say did I tell you Granty could crawl? Howard sits there watching then copies. Grant was so thrilled with himself! Sometimes one learns a thing first and sometimes the other. Did I tell you what Corinne said when I was bathing her last night? She . . ."

"Why doesn't the nurse bathe her?"

"Well, you see . . . she wanted me to. She said 'Don't choke my neck Daddy.' I was only washing it you know." He relaxes and laughs like anything. "Corinne's got temperament and brains. I might be her father but I say it. She's only two and a half and she can talk me to pieces. The way she arranges her little thoughts and sorts out the words she wants. She's got a feeling for words that girl. She copies everything we say. The other morning when we went in to see why Howard was crying we find him upside down at the bottom of the cot with both feet stuck through the rails, I don't know how he managed it, and I said 'No wonder!' And she goes round for the rest of the day saying to everything that happens 'No 'onder!' " He laughs like anything then pulls up suddenly. Suddenly . . . as though some memory within had struck him over the face.

"When I was out there and asked her where the boys were she said 'They's under-da-neaf da table toglevver.' Funny little kid. And when I got them out and combed their curls she said 'Mummie doos dat.'. . . . cute!

"Oh but listen to this! When I took her to Doctor John the other day to check up on her tonsils and he looked down her throat she said 'Don't look down my cough. I'n only a little girl. I'n going round da corner to 'chool 'esserday.' " He laughs again then that sudden pull-up. "I had the whole three of them to Doctor John the other morning; the twins for their injections and Corinne for this sleeping. He gave me some more sleeping stuff and last night she slept right through. I just couldn't believe it in the morning. Let's hope it lasts this time. The boys are marvellous sleepers, all night and we never hear them."

"She could do with more clothes Corinne."

"Do you think so dear?"

"That Tartan wool . . . it was nice but . . . but it could be a little shorter Gordon. She's got good legs."

"Her mother always liked her dresses down to her knees like that. Her mother was . . . is . . . a great one for modesty. She said . . . says . . . that modesty is the most important thing in a girl. She was always teaching Corinne that before she . . ."

"How is your wife Gordon?"

A long pause. "The vomiting has returned."

"We can't marry yet . . . for some time, for some time Gordon."

"Not for some time."

"No."

A sandfly or a mosquito or something bites my leg and I stoop to rub it. "Isn't it visiting hours at the hospital today?"

"This afternoon."

Silence.

"Brett's there. He looks after her so faithfully. He never misses a day whether it's visiting hours or not. It was . . . it was he who . . . I first heard about . . . all this from him. He . . ."

I scratch this leg, it's itchy. Below the hemline too. It might leave a mark. "Our wedding . . . it'll have to be a long time after . . . after. Not till the middle of summer."

He turns away. "Forgive me dear. I . . . I'm so short of sleep I'm beside myself." Tears again.

"I'll teach Corinne music. I'll start her at three. My father took me to the keyboard at three."

"I must not leave the babies too long without a mother dear."

"I can understand Corinne's position . . . all too well."

"Their Grandma is too old to mind them much longer. She says the waking in the night is killing her."

"Why doesn't the nurse do the waking?"

"She . . . I . . . she just doesn't wake that's all. She's never been married and had children. She doesn't know how to sleep with half the mind awake as it is when you've got babies. I used to sleep heavily when my wife was home but now . . . I stay half awake as she did. She still sleeps with only half her mind up there you know listening in case they wake. This nurse has no idea what it is . . . this alertness all

247

night and the alarm when you hear them. To hear a baby cry in the night . . . the alarm of it! You sleep with a feeling of urgency, of possible calamity all the time. But this nurse she sleeps like an irresponsible log. Dies for eight hours. We parents need the childless people, they can take the strain the next day. Crikey, the mess a small child can make of grown-up days. My temper these days at work, what with broken sleep . . . and the repercussions all through the businesses and staffs . . . the less said about it the better. Hugh plays a buffer all the time. I knew what I was doing when I took that boy although . . . although it was Brett who persuaded me . . . at the time I . . .

"But oh we just don't know what to do about this little thing's dreadful sleeping. Nor Doctor either. She used to sleep you know. Brett says she knows deep within her that all is not well. But she seldom speaks of her mother. Except to say that she went away on the bus-ee . . . the ambulance she means. Brett said she knows . . . that children do."

"Will I have to wake in the night to the children?"

He sinks down on the grass. "I'll do your waking in the night. It's only that girl. She gets out and gets into my bed. And you want to try sleeping with a two-year-old. If she would only keep her own side but it seems that she must be touching. I've had to block the top of the stairs in case she walks the wrong way. And then you see she's cross the next day and won't eat her food. I said to her this morning when we woke up 'You should stay in your own bed.' And she said 'I be a good girl when I'n big.' And I said 'Why don't you stay in your own bed?' And she said 'Mummie won't sing me.'" Tired tears again. "Can't we marry before midsummer?"

"I'm going to be . . . aa . . . occupied . . . till midsummer."

"Of course. Your music must come first. As it always will I promise you. I understand. We'll leave it till midsummer. As long as we can all be near you . . . sometime."

I stoop and gather one of the innocent pansies; little velvet things with no worries about sin. "You'll need to stop coming to see me Gordon until round about then. On account of . . . you, we don't want people talking. I'm all for propriety my-self."

"I told you I was going away. Taking the babies down to the South Island and Mother can supervise them there in her own home. I'd never be separated from them. Mother's breaking her neck to get back. She left the goat tied up and she said the vandals break her trees and her fowl have to run loose for food and her prize rooster visits ill-bred hens down the street for free. The Austrolop rooster was away for three days."

"How can you leave your businesses and your orchard and you'll miss making your float for the Blossom Parade."

"I'm opening a new branch down there. My managers can carry on here. They always do better with responsibility. Hugh ClanWilliam can do the personal contact work. He's marvellous at that sort of thing. People just eat out of his hand. Gosh his touch on the very worst of them! As for the blossom float . . ." sigh. "I'll be sorry to miss that. But my staffs love doing that sort of thing. All their wives show up and any spare husbands even the children and they all get to work on the blossoms. And the girls love dressing up in something ravishing and getting on the floats themselves . . . did I tell you who's going to be our Spirit of Spring? Elizabeth Dalgliesh. And the boys burst with ideas, and the men . . ."

"Then I won't be seeing you again till midsummer."

"I'll be flying up to see my wife. In the meantime Brett will mind her." A pause and he looks up anxiously. "As long as there *will* be a midsummer for us. And there will be, won't there dear. I'll leave you in Brett's care too. If you could only attend church more darling. You haven't come for some time. I know his preaching is not much but . . . it needn't be quite as bad as it is now. But he told me there was some vital element missing; some challenge from the congregation he can't do without. Some proud sinner he says who provokes the best in him."

"There are any number of sinners there to provoke him; proud or otherwise. He has told me so himself."

"I've never known who it is."

"What about his gift of God, Elizabeth? Doesn't she provoke him? Or has purity not the capacity to provoke?"

"Eliza provokes someone else. She's interested in Hugh ClanWilliam."

"Too bad."

"But I'd like you to return to church dear for my sake. I need to think of you cared for, visited, watched over, taught and belonging to something large and benevolent. No other body has the continuity of the church and its unfailing principled goodwill. I'd feel more at peace. I don't like to think of you entirely alone. And you haven't been looking yourself lately; not since you had that flu and I don't like that cough."

"I'll go back if *you* want me to. But not for a half-inch man. He doesn't like young people in his church, I can tell." He only likes them in an orchard where they have to listen to him endlessly. "He just likes his precious old grey-haired saints huddled towards the back. And some tepid purity in the choir."

"How can you say such a thing!"

"I can say it all right. That's what his exams are for. I couldn't ever pass anything like that and he knows it. Besides look at the things he says: 'Speak not in the hearing of a fool.' I'm tired of being a fool in that church. I'm never other than a cringing, guilty, iniquitous fool. I'm not used to the burden of sin."

"You mustn't think like that Germaine."

"That's not my real habitat, church. I'm treated differently in concert halls. No one calls me a fool in concert chambers. People clap for me at concerts, and try to be introduced and light my cigarettes and send me the loveliest flowers. Did anyone in that church of yours ever ask to be introduced or light my cigarette or bring me the loveliest flowers?"

"You must be fair dear. You've never let them know who you are."

"According to what I hear from the pulpit that shouldn't make any difference."

"Is this why you have not been to church? Because of . . ."

"People in my world don't talk about Master-Sentiments and battles of the church all the time and . . ."

"You don't have to equip yourself for any battle of the church. The dear old church can take it and has for the last twenty centuries. She thrives on her recurring crises. She . . ."

"And people in my world don't talk about speaking in the hearing of fools either. If we happen to be fools we like it. But I don't like my . . ." I just pull up in time. I don't like my Almighty Rival.

"If this is how he makes you feel I'll have a word with him. He's got to look after you when I'm away."

"I'm not joining the ranks of his miserable 'looked-afters!' I don't have to be locked up in the parsonage."

"He may be run down poor chap. He works too hard and he feels other people's pain too much. I'm only too well aware he feels mine. He suffers so much you know. So many people hate him. He does feel it. We've got to remember all that. Its bad luck he's so tough physically otherwise a coronary or an ulcer would have made him let up long ago. I've seen him in a bad state after returning from that hospital or from a round my word I have. Of course he's always done the worst of the rounds. I've seen him in the most dreadful despair . . . but let's not talk of these sad things now. My darling . . . I . . . that you should be for me I . . . before I go I must . . ." an arm about me . . . "You do believe I love you . . . Germaine . . ."

"Yes."

"I didn't know what worship was."

"I thought Christians did."

"I didn't know till now. It's the way you listen . . . those exquisite eyes . . . I worship those eyes."

"What will God say to that."

"He gave me this love."

"I thought I did."

"God is responsible for everything wonderful."

"All I know is his wrath."

"I only want to talk about you." His arms . . . "I must . . ."

"Not yet Gordon." I'm in no mood for anyone since you rejected me. Since the blue Chinese gown failed. Besides kissing Gordon involves a particular personal commandment concerning any man you mean to marry.

"My dearest love . . ."

"Gordon I . . . it would be wrong."

"I always knew you were noble."

"Don't Gordon please. Not yet."

"Just once . . . Germaine . . . just once, so I'll know."

"I'll kiss you first thing midsummer."

"But I can't stand it. I'm too tired to stand it. I must, must . . . so I'll know . . . know you love me . . . enough to begin on."

I offer my ballistic mouth briefly. "Yes quite enough to begin on. But I trust you enough to end up on."

"You're the very softest thing I've ever touched. I . . . I love you enough for both of us. For the whole four of us. I love you with all I am and have Germaine. At last I know what I've self-made myself for. I'll love you for the rest of my life and with the rest of my life; now that I know what my life is for. Germaine . . . once more . . . please . . ."

"No . . . no Gordon, we both understand why."

"We both understand my darling. But it's hard. Too hard for a man of my age . . . for a man who's already been . . .

252

been . . . married. But you wouldn't know those things. Anything about that. Its the most impossible thing I've ever had to do . . . to let you go now. How I'm to wait till . . ."

I release myself and scratch my leg.

"But that's too good for the jumble-stall dear!" he exclaims later within the studio. "What a beautiful garment! Chinese isn't it? But I've never seen you wear that. When would you wear a thing like that?"

"I don't want it."

"But there's nothing wrong with it. And who in the church would wear it? Even if they did find it cheap on a jumble-stall? You can't give this away Germaine."

"Can't I?"

"Keep it darling. Keep it for yourself. You must be stopped from making such an unnecessary sacrifice."

"You take it in to the jumble-stall Gordon, go on. Give it to one of those . . . to Mrs. John or Mrs. Dalgliesh or . . . to one of them anyway. I . . ."

I don't want it. It has failed. It is demoted. It's a reminder of my inaccurate technique.

"Ah well . . . I must get along. Is there anything you want my darling?"

"I wonder Gordon if . . . I mean could you get hold of another radiogram for me?"

"They're on the list of prohibited imports."

"But isn't there a black market or something?"

"That's something I've never dabbled in dear."

"You said you'd do anything at all for me. Here don't forget to take this gown." This gown . . . if only I could get rid of the memory of that failure as easily as get rid of the gown.

253

H EAR THE WORD of the Lord!" you challenge us the
following Sunday evening, "as it is contained in the book of
Amos!"

My inebriated blood runs cold and it is cold enough outside the far door of the church. I have parked my car two
blocks away, entered the street door of the hall nearby, passed
creeping through it, out into the back yard, into the back
rooms of the church itself and stand at the far door. I had no
intention of coming to church and I haven't actually . . .
not really. Through the crevasse however I see that many
others actually have. The nave is packed right up to the table
of the Lord's Supper and there are chairs in some of the
aisles. All sorts of hilarious idolaters from Babylon have put
down their work on the blossoms for the parade . . . goodness only knows why . . . and from where I furtively eaves-

254

drop I can see that insipid creature Eliza simpering in the choir. The main body of the church is at last in it.

" 'Thus saith the lord!' " you boom. Ooh . . . have you heard this word of the Lord? Don't tell me I've shocked Him into speech.

" ' "For three transgressions of Damascus, and for four, I will not turn away. the punishment thereof! Because they have thrashed Gilead with thrashing instruments of iron! But I will send a fire unto the house of Damascus which shall devour the palaces thereof!" ' " . . . Boom . . . boom . . . boom up in the vaulted ceiling and among the lofty pillars.

" 'Thus saith the lord!

" ' "For three transgressions of Tyrus, and for four, I will not turn away the punishment thereof! Because they delivered up the whole captivity to Edom, and remembered not the brotherly covenant! But I will send a fire on the walls of Tyrus which shall devour the palaces thereof!"

" 'Thus saith the lord!

" ' "For three transgressions of . . ." ' " We hear a lot of transgressions. We also hear a lot about the punishment that will not be turned away. Your voice does not descend once. The ancient districts of thirty centuries back showed real imagination and inventiveness of a high order in the choice of their transgressions. My own are amateur beside them.

" ' "Is it not even thus, O ye children of Israel? But ye commanded the prophets, saying Prophesy not!" ' "

At last your voice descends on its outspread wing until it is one of soft intimacy. You lean easily across the pulpit. "Let us pause here a moment my people. Let us pay Amos the normal courtesy we would pay any modern speaker by considering what he has said. How ancient is his prophesy? Could it apply to us? Could these thrashing instruments be tanks or ballistic missiles? Have we ourselves witnessed whole nations being delivered into captivity? Have we? Have we in the city remembered the brotherly covenant? Have we pursued our brother with a sword and cast off all pity? Have we seen out in the world anger tearing perpetually and nations keeping their wrath?"

Your voice drops more softly still. "Who in our time, in our own twentieth century, have ripped up the women with child that they might enlarge their border? How many of us here, in the city, in the country, in the world have despised the law of the Lord? And flouted his commandments? Have our lies caused us to err? Have we sold the righteous for silver? Has our century trampled the head of the poor in the dust? Do a man and his father go in unto the same maid? Surely, my people, surely . . . with all the modern replacements of Christianity . . . our morality has advanced beyond that. Now think, my people, think with me; to what extent does his prophesy apply?" Your voice rests upon the great Bible before you.

"What, my people," you croon with that childish innocence I know, "is there in our century likely to cause 'the sun to do down at noon'? What scientific power have we in our mortal hands that could 'darken the earth in the clear day'? What could 'turn all our feasts into mourning, and our songs into lamentation' to reduce us to sackcloth and baldness? What have our mighty ones in their hands to bring us 'to mourn as for an only son and our end on a bitter day'? Why should we not go on living in the houses we have built and drinking from our pleasant vineyards? How out of date is Amos, thirty centuries back?"

You straighten and pocket your hands and move about easily improvising. "Let us translate Amos into modern terminology for all our young ones here. The flight shall perish from the jet and the East and the West shall not strengthen their force. Neither shall he stand who handles the warhead; or the ballistic missile. And he that is swift of plane shall not save himself. And he that is courageous among the mighty shall flee away naked in that day.

256

"But no, my people, no. We cannot listen to Amos. Not thirty centuries back. Not a primitive herdsman from the mountains following his flock and gathering sycamore fruit . . . how much further advanced are we. Look at our education, our philosophies, our ethics. Look at our art and our science. How much more civilised we are! What is a prophet to us? Let us not listen to any word of God interpreted by anyone."

You glance briefly at your notes then find the bowl of spring flowers to address. "Indeed and indeed my people how could we have anything at all in common with that ancient wealthy nation to whom he preached in the market place? This people who crushed the poor and oppressed the needy, who lay upon beds of ivory stretching themselves upon couches, eating the lambs of the flock and the calves from the midst of the stall; drinking wine in bowls from slaves, chanting to the sound of the viol and anointing themselves with the finest oils; making burnt offerings of meat and peace offerings of fat beasts; welding themselves images from molten silver, and idols the work of craftsmen; luxuriating in their kingdom of flax, wool and oil, of vines, corn and fig trees, of cyprus, oak and elm, olive trees, fir trees, cedarwood and lilies; of silver, gold and ivory . . . what have we conceivably in common with this 'Lost Tribe of Israel' who were never seen again?"

Another glance at your notes. You lift a page and turn it over, then lean on your elbows towards us. "From the point of view of idolatry we have everything in common with Israel. We too burn incense to idols. The only difference I see is that occasionally in that country a prophet would arise to chide the people and guide them, interpreting for them the word of the Lord. Have we a prophet in this century with the power and poetry of Amos? To take up his position in the market place of this earth to chide and guide us all? Would we listen if we had? Or are we doomed to be known among the populations of other planets as the 'Lost Tribe of the Earth' who were never seen again?"

You take a little pace round the pulpit. "Maybe we have a prophet in our country. Thus saith the Government:

> " 'For three transgressions of New Zealand, and for four,
> We will not turn away the punishment thereof.
> Because you have spent forty-four million pounds on racing in one year and fifty-four million pounds on beer in one year.
> Is it not even thus, O ye children of New Zealand?
> But ye commanded the Party, saying Prophesy Not!
> But we will send an earthquake of taxes unto New Zealand which shall devour the palaces hereof.
> Thus saith the Government.' "

Delighted laughter from the congregation which is hastily silenced. You smile to yourself modestly then continue robustly. "Prophets are two a penny. Why doesn't one of us stand up in the market place of New Zealand; in the Civic Square in Auckland, Courtenay Place in Wellington, the Cathedral Square in Christ church or the Octagon in Dunedin?

> " 'Thus saith the Church:
> For three transgressions of New Zealand, and for four,
> God may not turn away the punishment hereof.
> for we smack each other up every night when the pubs have closed at six,
> and in broad daylight we speed head-on upon each other;
> we spend multimillions over the years on horses, pubs and possessions,
> we elect schoolboys to our Parliaments

who degrade the English language
and debase the dignity of debate;
we penalise originality,
we crucify sensitivity,
we sentence our artists to ostracism and exile,
we allow the pollution of God's holy air in the Pacific,
we habitually despise the law of the Lord
and profane His holy name.
Is it not even thus, O we children of New Zealand?
Yet we command the Church, saying Prophesy Not!
But God may send another earthquake unto our country
    which shall devour the palaces hereof!
Thus saith the Church.' "

No laughter this time. New Zealanders don't like earthquakes. You spread your two hands out separately upon the Bible before you like two people at variance with each other:

"I wonder, my people, if the time will come in our century before it is too late, before the sun goes down at noon, before the earth darkens in a clear day, before all our feasts and Blossom Parades are turned into mourning as for an only son, before our songs become lamentation, before we all end on a bitter day, when a prophet of twentieth-century vintage will stand up in the market place of the Earth and speak without fear like Amos the Word: 'Seek good and not evil, that ye may live.' "

Maybe your God will not forgive me and will deal with me in the time of His anger but with your voice in its fullness, the sermon in its fullness and you in your fullness . . . as I slink back round the dark corners . . . I ache with the madness amorous. "There is no God," says the fool in my heart. *"There is no God!"* screams Baal in my heart.
Thus saith I.

Here is the Amos sermon of the evening before reported almost in full and an editorial answering it. I settle down and read it in the old French chair when I come in from the orchards. It holds forth about New Zealand though small and isolated doing more to help others than some of the larger countries. "Has the Reverend gentleman," it inquires, "ever heard of the Colombo Plan? Why doesn't he break into scriptural verse over our millions of pounds' assistance to Southeast Asian countries? From a nation of just over two million? Is this burning incense to idols? Or incense to love?

"All these humble, unsung and unprophesied efforts of ours towards our neighbours can hardly be 'despising the law of the Lord.' Is not the law of the Lord the law of Love? We respect the inspiration of a man of God but must the inspired word be so wholly unrelated to reason?

"You ignore the good in us and proclaim the evil.
Is it not even thus, O ye man of God?
Yet ye command the scientists, saying, Prophesy not!
But New Zealand may send an earthquake of ridicule
 unto the Church
Which will devour the palaces thereof.
Thus saith the City.
" 'O thou seer! Flee thee away into Judah and there eat bread and dictate alone to a scribe. But prophesy not again' in this city."

Reluctantly but with an "absolutely have to" compulsion I wade through the correspondence during the week. It seems to find some place in the city mind, although hardly contesting the argument about whether the Maoris should be included in the All Black Football Team to travel to South Africa. Nor does the furious controversy over the City Water Fluoridation Experiment give way to the City Morals Fluoridation Experiment, nor the preparations for the Blossom Parade to the progress of the Sentiment Parade. But it does hold ground for a while and I learn more about you in these letters, as a minister, an actor or a mere half-inch man, than can be good for any mere parishioner; and more about religion than I ever learnt from you.

I achieve the end of this correspondence; watching the Battle of the Church from a front seat relieves somewhat my own private battle. As far as an idolater can see no facet of the subject of good and evil appears to be left uncovered. Every aspect is cautiously examined except the one at the root of it all: that it was I, the transgressor alone at Three Trees, twisting in the white furnace of thirst, I, who in bringing human passion so near you loosened the word of your God.

Maudite soit la nuit aux plaisirs éphémères
Où mon ventre a conçu mon expiation.

H

UGH CLANWILLIAM has me on his tough visiting list now; I'm too tough apparently for you.

He walks with me through the orchards one late afternoon, after music, Tuesday I think it is, just as you used to do and talks about himself as you used to do, through acres of massing blossom. Remember how we walked down these aisles . . . But then the bloom was not full. You should see it now. In this orchard they're white but over the stile they're pink. Not a colour of mine pink but I can take it like this. Stoned fruit the pink and pipped fruit the white, all tucked away securely behind the poplar and Lawsoniana breakwinds like a country behind a curtain, safely undisturbed by gales. Clouds and clouds of blossom above the head and around. Skies full of blossom as I saw in a dream, blossoms pink and blossoms white, myriad petals a-massing, the whole vaulted spring sky full of clouds of blossom, revolving spiralling gyrating in slow impressive dignity and the music in my mind of voices singing "in pastures green he leadeth me the quiet waters by." Blossoms and singing in a dream I saw like some grand royal nuptial . . . I brush my eyes I brush my blue eyes. . . .

You'd like this now mon cher. The avenues have the silence and holiness of your church even to the choirs of birds. The temple of spring, the temple of spring, the temple of spring. There are still late bees out too. I love their hum don't you? A round soft sound with no lethal edges to it. I think I could do with no other music for the rest of my life but the sound of these birds and bees. I wish when I was born I had been dumped in a spring orchard in New Zealand rather than on a bellowing grand in Paris. I could have endured inner music like this if I had to endure it at all. Only birdsong it would have been then and the chords of these sinless bees. But the tone of Hugh's voice has changed and his subject too. I make an all-out effort to listen since it is about me now and I brush my eyes. . . . "It's so out of character for me," he is saying, "to be deliberately and consciously boring; but I can't regret what I've said."

"Ooh I might try it, I'm tired enough to. But that's enough of the Master-Sentiment. Come back with me to the studio now and we'll have a master-drink."

"I can't stay Gomer. I've got to . . ."

"Don't be silly. How long is it since you've tasted real French Pernod? There's some in there."

"We're preparing the floats for the Blossom Parade; I've got a hand in four. One from each firm, one from the orchard and we're having a go at one from the church. I promised the boss I'd see to his and I'm determined to be in on the church float what with Eliza featured upon it. Besides I've promised to pick up Brett on the way home and another thing I want an early dinner so that I can get down to my Baddies afterwards. They . . ."

"There's something plebeian in your avidity for work, *I* think."

" 'Work keeps at bay three evils: vice, boredom and need.' "

"You're turning into another boring moralist Hugh. It's the work of that half-inch man." We climb back over the stile into the white orchard again and make our way up the aisles. My matadors are black with long broad white perpendicular stripes and my sweater has a dragonfly on it. Right across the front with wings outspread and glaring eyes and . . . "Oh my inside when I think of that man! Whatever I try to call him. If ever I get over him my organs never will; they no longer remember their original places. They've lost themselves for good."

"I hope," says Hugh, "that you heard his sermon on Amos."

"Yes I did."

"He heard the word of God that night. He was radiant after that sermon. He wandered about among the people after church as though he were drunk. His eyes shone just like yours. He kept on muttering to himself 'I've never preached like that before.' He paced about with his head down and his hands in his pockets and his black robe flowing not listening to what anyone said. Then he'd stand still and stare through the trees and lights and shadows and sometimes out to the traffic. 'I've never preached like that before.' And I haven't told you this. He saw your car pull out and the way he just stood and stared with that blazing light in his face. He watched you edging through the traffic to the corner and when you pulled up there at the stop sign he took some steps towards you. And when you moved on he kept on walking. Then he stood and stared at where you had been. As if you had something to do with it."

"Funny isn't it."

"Later walking back to the parsonage together he told me that some violent shock he had had . . . how did he put it . . . had loosened the word of God. He said 'I know now what God's purpose for me is. All I need is courage.'"

"What he needs is another shock."

"But where from? There's something going on in his life I don't know about. This violent stimulus for instance . . . I don't know the origin of it. And he really is preaching better these days. Look at the growing congregations.

"Somebody told me I forget who that people are going to his church only for the sensationalism of it. He says such outrageous things. That they find in him such a responsive target for criticism. Look at all that in the paper last week. He's something for the city to play with."

"He could be too. But the fact remains that he's preaching better, whether people admit it or not."

"You'll never get me to admit it."

"Well why do you hang round?"

"That's a question I can never answer."

"Tell me straight . . . do you love him?"

"Me? I hate him!"

"I am not wholly convinced. You French are a funny people; you pride yourselves on your logic but you have a positive genius for enshrouding an issue. No wonder you run into consequences."

"I'm tired of your moralising Hugh; and that's not enshrouding any issue. You're getting more like him every day. What you want is some Pernod. That's your trouble these days. Men get so boring when they're sober. Come inside and make me laugh. I'll play the new chanson for you."

"The sight and smell of that stuff utterly nauseates me now."

"Romeo. I'll consider trying to do what you say . . . all this new leaf business . . . if you come and have a drink with me."

"We're working on the floats I said. I mean to show the boss First Prize. Besides don't forget I've got a job; half-past eight to half-past five, forty-hour week and all that, paid every Friday."

"Do you or do you not want me to stop all this kiss-me-wrong business?"

He looks at me appraisingly and speaks in a practical dry staccato. "It is now Tuesday. I'll come out next Monday morning and if you have done two things . . . been to church and not kissed anybody . . . *anybody* . . . in the meantime, I'll have a drink with you; if it turns me inside out."

"Not be kissed for a week! But Dezso is bringing my dress tonight. And how can I get past Wednesday with Léon at the National Orchestra, and past Dezso at a party afterwards! What if Johnnie comes to see me! And what do you think Fridays and Saturdays are made for? As for Thursday and Sunday . . . could you go unkissed for a week? The prospect is worse than the dentist."

"It's a different thing altogether with men."

"As for church! My flirtation with religion is over."

"Those are my terms," he says.

"Ooh come inside and be realistic."

A spring afternoon of milky innocence with fruit blossom breaking in the vase. The scented bee-humming hours insist on their sinlessness including the whole human race and hell itself; I feel as pure as a babe on the bottle. I run across to the keyboard for my answer to everything; my routine comment on all. "I say Brother listen to this. L'Élixir. I swear you'll hold your breath from start to finish. You've never . . . oooh!"

"What's the matter?"

"Oooh . . . I'm . . . you've never heard anything like it."

"Are you sick?"

"Some more flu I suppose."

266

"Aren't you going to play it?"

"All right. Stand back. Give me some room. Open that window Hugh. I mean this. You'll soon know why I followed him from Paris."

"I know you even less Germaine."

Through the window are the listening trees and beyond them the lofty breakwinds. You can still see through these breakwinds, the cauldron of colour there. It is still there as before I began. It's hard to believe it's the same. Same trees, same colour, same breakwinds. That's what always amazes me, that the world should still be the same after one of Léon's chansons. I brush my eyes . . . "What were you saying Brother?"

"I wasn't saying anything. But I'm going to. No I've never heard anything like it. You change when you are playing though. The way you assume the personality of the music and are no longer Gomer. Seeing and hearing you on those keys is a frightening experience. Such extraordinary virtuosity . . . I'd go starry if I didn't know you so well. Thank you Germaine de Beauvais. It's a great privilege to hear you. An artist of your magnitude could possibly be allowed a few aa . . . vagaries."

"Depravities is what you mean; why not say it? I have no moral pretensions."

He doesn't reply and runs his hand over the back of his hair.

"I wasn't so conscious of my flair for depravity when Corinne was here; she made me feel innocent again; just as the orchards do."

"They seemed to have to go. It was the Grandma; what she says in that family is law . . . or has been with Mrs.

267

Hood in hospital. As late as going up the gangway she was still telling me it was all on account of a rooster of hers. It seems she owns an Austrolop rooster. She said her neighbour down South had written and said she had called in the Society for the Prevention of Cruelty to Animals to see to her neglected stock. They had already let the goat loose on the hills and they were going to give the fowls to the butcher at once. But every time they came to get them this Austrolop was honeymooning down the street. What old Gord's up against is a virile rooster. An whole new branch of his Hardware coming into being on account of this libidinous Austrolop and an whole new breed of Austrolops. And an whole new breed of goats on the hill. So you see they all had to go."

"That's all very funny but I must lie down."

"Here pull this eiderdown over you."

"Thank you Brother. I've done very little practice. J'aurai de la peine à travailler aujourd'hui."

He sits on the end of the bed. "It's usually a bad sign when you collapse into French."

"I can collapse into anything with you; you're a gentleman."

"I'm a gentleman in the worst sense of the word."

"I wish I were dead when I feel like this. I could cheerfully open an artery. It's not deep you know, the radial artery. Just under the skin, just here. Could I do it with a nail file do you think? What I need is . . ."

"Don't talk like that with me about."

"You'd talk like that too if you felt like me. There's no other way to talk."

"Have you had any food today?"

"Ooh if I could only have some *real* food. And another thing, why don't people eat outside here? I know a table under a vine looking out across the Seine . . . you can see the square towers and the spires of Notre-Dame. I remember having some courgettes there."

"What are they."

"Ooh I have been craving them lately."

"What are they like?"

"They're little marrows stuffed with . . . what are they stuffed with again. Um . . . small peppers and onions . . . spiced. And you can have dinner on the Seine too at night on the little steamers. They ply up and down under the bridges. The Seine is floodlit in the evening. Under the Pont Neuf and the Pont St.-Michel and the Pont Alexandre III. They're all lit up in the floodlights. And under the bridges there are young people making love and derelicts settling down for the night wrapped in newspapers you can see them and . . . then when you've finished coffee you go out on deck and look at Notre-Dame above the trees . . . ooh the way they serve food at home."

"Yes."

"And there was a place we used to go to called the Quail Song where you can get stuffed aubergines . . . I've really been craving them lately . . . no I haven't been eating to-day . . ."

Later, "Any cigarettes about?"

"On the mantelpiece there. Have some of that wine too."

"No thanks. Gomer . . . you'll have to give up your playmates as I said before. Between them they're killing you off."

"You're apt to forget I've been married."

"Y-yes . . . still I've got to start somewhere however misguided. So do you, my dear. Start off with dropping Doctor John."

"He may have already dropped me. He didn't come and attend me when I rang and nothing will make me go to his surgery with his gossipy nurse there. But apart from him being a good doctor . . . one who knows me well you know . . . he's no loss. His technique was factory-cut and his vocabulary too. I like a man with . . ."

"Good. One struck off the list. Next, this demonic expatriate of yours. He's doing you the most harm I think."

"I do wish I could. But there's not another teacher to touch him. My father has said so. And I couldn't stand anyone else on the chansons. They're all mine. They're the only children I could bear to have. Pull that blind down will you? Ooh but his soul exhausts me . . . all this absinthe he's been getting hold of."

"I wouldn't like you to find yourself in the position where you would have to marry him."

"What do you mean *have* to!"

"There's such a thing as becoming pregnant."

"Don't say that word!"

"Somebody's got to say it."

"You don't . . . at this particular moment."

"But everybody knows that even the most accomplished of techniques have been known to . . . there's so much in sex that is unforeseeable."

"Nothing will ever make me marry any man I don't want to whatever the position I find myself in foreseeable or otherwise you can take that straight *nothing*. I live in my own way. Let alone that lunatic. Ooh you don't know him as I do. He's smashed two radiograms so far; they're on the list of prohibited imports. He argues he's a genius and that he spends most of his time in another world and that I keep him in touch with reality and that he'll go mad if I don't marry him soon. As if marriage was the answer to anything. Let him go mad let him. As long as it is not at Three Trees. But I'm not saying it's a . . . it's . . . all this is a worry you know Brother. I don't think I deserve it do you?"

"Neither you nor any of your playmates are getting any worse than what a crowd of hedonists deserve. Passion has a function in life but none of you can see it, or would do anything about it if you could see it. You all help yourselves to it rapaciously and put nothing of sacrifice or faithfulness or common purpose back in, which in essence is marriage. No wonder your affairs become empty in time . . . episodes without productivity or continuity. Which in essence is promiscuity. Or to use the more powerful Bible word . . ."

"Don't use that word I don't like it. And anyway Brother this is not church. This is my own habitat." I almost retch then lie back still. "Some burdens should be thrown to the ground I think don't you? That's what you said once. You said that loving life too much was a ridiculous weakness. You said it was the most disastrous of our inclinations. You said it was silly to go on bearing a burden that should be thrown to the ground. I remember all you said in your pit . . . ooh no it was down at the jukebox joint . . . yes that's right . . ."

"Dangerous talk Gomer. ANYWAY . . . we'll shelve him for the moment. Do you have to play with this traffic super?"

"I haven't noticed my driving improved . . . although my New Zealand vocabulary has. 'Fair go, pop in, she's right' and such. But—but I don't know that you are right about dropping my playmates Brother. All I want is a change. After a while they get so boring. The importer is young and fearfully funny and as for Dezso," I manage to smile, "he's my dream come true. I wouldn't have anything to wear to the Orchestra without knowing him socially. No . . . no Brother; it's true men are maddening and . . . and expensive and . . . and of course exhausting but . . . but I'm not prepared to drop them for a single moment on any of those accounts."

" 'Whoredom and wine taketh away the heart.' "

"I hate that word I said."

I get up and accompany him to the gate though. I throw the old practise cardigan over my shoulders and we walk together up the drive, our feet crunching on the fine gravel Gordon has spread. On either side pansies look up with Corinne's trusting eyes. "I've a feeling I won't see Corinne again."

"Nonsense you're supposed to be marrying them all."

"Supposed to be."

"That's interesting."

More slow steps between the pansies. We pause together at the gate. "Well," he says after a moment, "I must be going."

"You're always going," I whine.

"You used to leave me in the early days outside the church."

"I know. But stay a little longer Hugh."

"It used to be I saying that to you."

"There's no need to tease me. You'll be at the Orchestra tomorrow night?"

"If someone hires me a suit. In any case I'll be here on Monday morning."

"I like you being here Hugh; don't go yet."

"That's very sweet of you but I've got to pick up Brett at a quarter past five and it's now . . . six minutes past."

"Where is he?"

"Where is he? Do you want to know where he is? I'll tell you. He's sitting under a willow on the riverbank staring at the water."

"What about his rounds?"

"He hasn't been on a round since that showdown in the press. He's carrying on like a child about it. He hasn't even been up to see Mrs. Hood. I went myself. I've also called on your illustrious Maestro. And I've been to see the Johns . . . and here I am seeing you. I run this church now."

"What's wrong with him?"

"All he says . . . since that editorial telling him to flee away, prophesy not, all he says is that the Master no longer speaks. He says he has lost his courage. You'll find a difference in him. Now I must go."

"It's time you weaned yourself from that man. You're losing your own identity. Baal and I are missing you. Coddled up in his parsonage . . . you boob!

"I'm not saying I haven't had enough of the parsonage. But it's not so easy to get board. The thing is," he strokes his hair, "to find a home where the mother is not too young and the daughters not too old." He vaults the gate; a thing you can't do.

I open it laughing and follow him to his car, the same Jowett-Javelin. "You know what I like about you Hugh? You're young like me. It's a rest to have a visitor who is young like me. The others are all double my age. I'm a generation out in my playmates." He takes his seat and I lay a hand upon the smart sill; the scene outside the church at the beginning of our acquaintance in reverse. "You always listen to what I say. All the others do the talking and expect me to listen. They rave about my listening eyes then get under way. I wish I had eyes like pinheads."

A towering sheep truck with double decks thunders down the road home from the saleyards. When it has gone and I have taken my hands from my head I hear him saying ". . . I know I'm young but youth can be a limitation. I'm too young to influence you."

"Of course you can't. I can't suddenly and fundamentally alter my style. It would be bad musicianship. In any case . . . to change would presuppose shame and I think shame is just plain damn silly. The only . . . I—I . . . my only sin is that I was born at all. The only change I want is in playmates."

"I don't think I'm trying to change you; I just want you to try another view of life. You—you see . . . you . . . it's just that you give depravity a chance all the way to prove itself but you don't give good a chance. How can good make headway? It's not what I call fair. You don't even see Baal for what he is. How can anyone see their idol properly when they're bowing their heads to the ground at its feet? Oh but

I'm out of my depth. You're too tough for my visiting list too. Brett should do his own work. At least he knows what a human being should be."

"I doubt if his idea of what we should be has anything to do with a human being."

"At least he manages to keep his brutish pleasures in their place! One is either an animal or isn't; he at least isn't. He makes do with the glory of God."

"I still prefer my brutish pleasures to the glory of any god."

"I can't win." He lays fingers on the key. "You have an insufficient sense of doom Gomer. You live with a carelessness that suggests we can die any number of times whereas we all die but once." He turns on the ignition just as I used to do and touches the sensitive starter. "Be a good girl Germaine is all I ask and is all I've a right to ask." His ocean eyes look ahead along the road. But as the engine moans and the car moves I hang on as he used to do.

"Hugh," I say, "stop."

"What is it?"

"I—I . . . don't know."

He turns his eyes upon me. They don't swerve or blink or stray. They're wide and deep and full of the storm of the ocean. For once my own eyes are really listening and not just appearing to be. "Go on, say what it is you haven't said," I say. "People like me can't stand people like you going away full of what they haven't said. I got too much of that from *him*."

"I'll come out on Monday Gomer." He gets out of the car again. "Got a cigarette? On Monday morning. Thanks. Not to have a drink with you but to . . . to see if I'm prepared to support your marriage to Gordon." He begins pacing and throwing round his hands. "Unless you change your ways I'll oppose it. I'm in the position to. I'm not too young for that. When it comes to the future life of four souls, three of them barely taken body, against the self-indulgence of one, I'll

274

oppose anything. And a marriage with no give and take in it, purely for what you can get out of it, with no thought of sacrifice or love rates no higher than just that: indulgence. God is reputed not to like self-indulgence and neither do I. Here at least I see my way and d'you know what it is? Never to let you enter that family with your hands as they are. You're engaged to Gordon so you belong to him. You have no right, no moral or decent right, to sleep in other men's arms. I myself will not have it. Gordon only has to know your record and he would never allow you within the length of an island of his children. So you can make up your mind about it . . . and you've got until next Monday."

"Go on . . . I can take it."

"It's not too late Gomer. There's trouble in the Johns' home, a happy progressive home it was, but if you leave Doctor alone it could right itself. A public divorce will settle all your dreams of having Corinne . . . however much you love her. Think that over. Monsieur Montigny has not broken out yet but I don't know how long he'll last with the torture you're putting him through. Who else . . . all the other minor supports . . ."

"I say Brother tell me. What would . . . which is the . . . what should I actually . . . What course should I take I mean, what should be done so that I can have Corinne?" I lay the second hand on the sill. "I . . . I—I'm prepared to try anything at all, anything at all so that I can have Corinne."

"What *should* be done is that you use the Reverend Guymer for his original purpose. You *should* go to him as your priest and confess your life and ask God's forgiveness and help and . . . and take another view of life. But I'm not in the position to advise it. At the moment he's a dead loss at private counsel. Ever since that blaze-up in the press. He can't get over that bit about 'Flee thee away into Judah and there eat bread and dictate alone to a scribe. But prophesy not again in this city.' He says it has so upset him that although God resumed speaking to him He is silent once more. He can't get off the subject of himself and about the Master no longer speaking. You'll never get him to listen to you. Trying to get through to him these days is like cutting through high-tension wire."

Silence but for the engine then he continues; "Besides the tension between the two of you now . . . it makes the whole thing impossible. There shouldn't be any of this personal relationship between a priest and his parishioner. It's always been his worst weakness. He himself stands between God and His people."

"Well what shall I do then Brother?"

"All you can do is stop dead in your tracks. Under your own power. I'm trying to help but I know I'm not much. Listen. It's simple; stop sleeping with men like an animal if you want to marry Corinne's father. That's plain isn't it? No doubt you will find it uncomfortable but . . . but you won't *die*."

I lift a hand to a cheek. "I'll try to do it Brother; not on account of any . . . any Almighty God but . . . but so that I'll be a good mother for Corinne."

He slumps back in the seat and breathes the words, "If I were Brett I'd say 'Bless you.'"

It's growing chilly and I return inside. I find the fire nearly out and I bring in some wood from the box Gordon has put outside the door and pile it on, one piece upon the other neatly so that the flame can breathe. Then I crouch down closely before it until the flames come to life . . . I won't make a meal tonight . . . and I won't do anything about getting ready for Dezso; he can try the dress on me for the Orchestra tomorrow night . . . try it on as I am . . . I don't know where my energy has got to.

There are some lovely variations to the Lullaby in my head and I feel Corinne in my arms. It's a change from feeling you. I feel her on my knee and it's a release of a kind; a sensation undisruptive to my organs. A rest from my terrible enslavement. Her limbs are soft and flexible and fit into me and about me. Now she moves into another position, her arms round my neck and mine round her body. Now her legs draw up and I encircle them too. My arms gather her all up in a bundle and my face in her tummy, and her head behind mine, our hair confusing. Now another fluid move, cheek to cheek, one arm round her shoulders and the other round her bottom, encircling, entwining, clasping, flowing. A little kiss in her neck, a little kiss on her knee . . . alive, soft, yielding, claiming, warm, trusting and mine; much more than mine, she's me. I didn't know what arms were for till I knew this child. . . .

Then I wake and find the flames high and that she is not here after all and my arms are empty again.

We must be together all the time; first thing in the morning and last thing at night. And all night of every night sleeping in the same room. I must know she is always near me. It's I, not a paid nurse, who will wash her and dress her and feed her and hear what she says. It will be I who chooses which dress she wears in the morning, who does up her shoes and combs her hair. It's I who will go shopping and buy her pyjamas and slippers. She'll go hand in hand for walks with me and not with some well-paid stranger. I'll play with her in the sand and on the swing and on the bars in the playground. I'll teach her little hands to play the pianoforte and I'll sing to her every night. And when she cries it will be I who pick her up and kiss her. We'll never be apart not for one minute of the day and her little life will be part of mine.

As for three transgressions of Germaine and for four God will not turn away the punishment thereof . . . he will when I meet him socially.

"Have you heard of the divorce coming up?"

"Whose?"

"The Johns'."

"Jesus."

"Don't say that."

"J-E-S-U-S C-H-R-I-S-T!"

Silence. "You . . . heathen."

Someone in the crowded foyer bumps me and my gold lighter clatters to the marble floor. Hugh picks it up and offers it to me. "It's the talk of the church so you might as well know. No one knows its you though . . . so far. Here take this lighter. I've picked it up twice. Don't look like that. Don't let everybody see you. I was a fool to have told you in here. Why didn't I . . ."

"Does *he* know."

"No. Stan was telling me at band practise last night then he got on his motorbike no one could stop him and off he boomed to a place a hundred miles off. I rang the police there to . . ."

"Light this damned thing will you."

"Well hold your hand still. I rang the police to hold him till I . . . Listen you've got consequences coming Gomer. You're going to meet this magistrate of yours and not socially either. If not a Supreme Court Judge and I don't see any man of law in this country being played either even by eyes like yours. You might have to get to know God socially and try playing him. I don't want to see anything as exotic as you out of sight in a pit . . . what a loss to Mammon. What's the matter? I thought you'd laugh this off. I thought all your reactions were surface. How was I to know you could . . . could . . . has something sounded your fastnesses? Don't tell me you . . ."

"There's too much noise in here. I can't stand it I can't stand it . . . I can't stand it. . . ."

J'étalerai mes baisers sans remords
Sur ton beau corps . . .

I FIND MYSELF DRESSING on Saturday evening with care never mind why. White georgette over a black lace brassière with a wide deep peasant frill from shoulder to shoulder that you don't quite see through yet do. Ballistic lipstick and Strontium perfume and the blossomed skirt con brio. People like me must do something when the consequences of sin accumulate and clothes is all I can think of. Besides you did tell me to come when I needed you. "Is it not even thus, O ye man of God?"

It can't be done without high-impulse fuel of course and it can't be done without two. It can't be done I find without three for that matter nor can I manage without four. Indeed to infuse the sparkling insight missing from this lifeless act of reason I may need more en route. I've got to supply some form of propulsion when the "absolutely have to" is missing and I'll do anything to win Corinne.

It is a fortunate thing isn't it that Gordon has widened this drive. Long may Gordon widen my drives! Woo-oops! here's the Citroën across the road in the ditch at the far side! . . . how did this happen? How can I get out again? I'll need another cocktail. Magistrates, I consider pouring another glass, don't appreciate how necessary drinking is to driving. How can one get out of a ditch without it? Now which is the gear again . . . oooh! Here I am back in the driveway! What an astonishing thing! Where *is* this elusive road? I swear there was one here this morning. . . .

I happen to know where your parsonage is. Happen? All right I *know* where the parsonage is; I chanced to drive by one day. Chanced? Very well I intentionally drove by one day. One day? All right then if you want the facts I know where the parsonage is very well since I have often . . . OFTEN! . . . wittingly driven that way. How uncomfortable accuracy is!

I move off through the village carefully since I really mean to arrive. I drive slowly through the miles of orchards in their pink-and-white bridal array, acres of wedding bouquet for someone, along the length of the main thoroughfare already being decorated for the Blossom Parade, beneath the strings of flags and coloured lights flung across overhead from side to side, between the shop fronts lavish in bloom, turn up the long side street to the right for many shadowy blocks, wind through the residential area to the far outskirts and brake beneath some trees. Ah . . . got this far!

You live in a white two-storied, roughcast house with nothing higher than a few shrubs around it. No fence, no trees, no hedge, no nothing. Have you so little to hide? Why leave these street trees out here then if it's privacy you do not want? From my car you are already in plain view through an open window writing at your desk. Why not take down the outer walls as well? We could all help in the preparation of a sermon from the street; toss you some rhetoric in passing.

Ooh but trust me to pick sermon night! But how can this be sermon night? Isn't it Thursday you work out those things? Or have you been working on it ever since Thursday? Anyway an interruption from me wouldn't hurt it. Anything I did to a sermon of yours could not but vastly improve it. VASTLY! Now come on Germaine we're going in . . . or do I need another Rocket? I do need another after all; they take such time to accumulate.

In time, my own time, I leave the party and approach the tall white ascetic house over the grass with the heartbeat of city within me. The warm spring evening is softly promising the story of summer to come, the first half of summertime anyway. There is drama talk and passion in the air, if not outright obsession. The horns of the city are talking it, the music of a band and the wistful bells of a church . . . mon Dieu what steep steps! This one, both feet. Next one both feet. This one . . . this one . . . is this the last? It is I do believe. Congratulations I'm on the porch. What a large chaste door. I knock all over your sermon.

Sounds within. Disturbed sermony sounds; now what have I done? It is too late to vanish . . . the door opens. Here is an unknown version of you. A humble man in soft home clothes, soft dull greys, unpressed . . . are you shaven? And a soft home dignity, a domestic voice and lighting it all pleasurable surprise. "Good EE-vening, Mrs. aa . . . Jones!"

I need another Rocket.

"Come IN Mrs. aa . . . Jones."

I do come IN and follow you into your study; furnished in frightful taste. How-can-I-get-out-of-here-again! I've made a mistake, I've made a . . .

"Sit HERE, Mrs. Jones, or HERE. If you don't mind waiting while I finish this."

I swing round to the door, skirt swishing, but you are here

281

before me. You commandeer my georgette arm and draw me back. "My OTHER work can wait. Try this chair then, or THIS."

"No thank you sir I'll try THIS." It is a low chair THIS and for some reason you take a high one, and put on an admirable show of easiness.

"ANYWAY," you lean back, "how ARE you?"

I dare not say so am silent. The light is unshaded and far too harsh and I lower my face from it. Neither of us speaks for a moment if you can call half an hour a moment. At length you appear to think of something. "I am very glad you have come to see me."

"I'm sorry to disturb your sermon sir. I should go away. I thought Thursday was sermon night."

"It is. But this has continued since Thursday, and for some time before. I've been thinking about it for weeks and working on it for nights. Amos again. I've wanted to deliver it for Sundays but I haven't had the courage."

"A pity." I lift a hand and shade my eyes.

"I don't know whether it is a pity or not."

"I'm sure it's a very frightful pity."

"Are you?"

"It's always a pity not to say what you want to. I've been wanting to say something myself. I've been thinking about it for weeks too, and working on it for nights but nothing remote like Amos. Something much more uncomfortably near. To you I've wanted to say it. But *I* haven't had the courage."

"That's a pity too."

"Besides I wanted to know also before it was too late what it is to visit the Minister of the Church in his original capacity of priest. Something new to people like me."

"Bless you for that." You lift one knee upon the other and fold your hands upon it. "There are some things in us all that must be told some time."

282

"Yes."

"I myself, whenever I meet you . . . just to see you . . . feel the weight of all the unsaid."

"That's what I feel. I want to tell you everything about . . ."

"This tremendous burden of the UNSAID! I can hardly endure it at times. I'm so glad you came tonight."

"I came because I want to be good enough for someone I've come to love even though she's very small. I mean I want to take another view of living. I've come to you to . . ."

"The insupportable unsaid! Not only in my relations with people," you rise and start on your pacing, "but with the population as a whole. With people as a city, a country, a world. There's so much hatred for me; I saw it in the press. I know how the Prophets felt. I know how Amos felt. But he had the courage to rise and say it in spite of the feeling against him. I haven't, I haven't, although God does drive me. There's that sermon lying there; felt for years, thought over for weeks and worked upon for nights. But where's the man to deliver it?" Pace, pace . . . pace. "I flee me away into Judah and . . . prophesy not."

"I want to say something too. To you sir as a priest. The consequences of my sin are beyond me. I can no longer surmount them. I'm going to lose the one person I've ever managed to love. I . . ."

"I'm at the crossroads," pace . . . pace . . . "the CROSS-ROADS! I must go one way or the other! Either I speak this sermon or I slither back into the morass of mediocrity and compromise that every parson knows and from which I am laboriously raising myself. I must face the hatred of people or give way abjectly before it. I must continue to do the thing they hate; help them against their will, or take the line of least resistance. People hate help. 'The poor hates the hand that gives it bread.' This is my crisis: fear of what people say, fear of losing my status, fear of losing my security, fear of ostracism, fear of censure, fear of everlasting loneliness! Fear of everything except what Amos had to fear; thrown alive into a pit, sawn in half or crucified upside down. This extreme necessity to speak and the bitter price of it!"

"Do listen to me Mr. Guymer; I'll never get myself here again. It costs too much in cocktail. This means no practise tomorrow. Listen there's a child I want to be moral enough for. I'm tired of burning incense to idols. I want . . .

"I also burn incense to idols! I'm afraid to lose materially. I'll lose ecclesiastically as well! Amos had nothing to lose in this way. Not in my twentieth-century way. He only had his life to lose. A man in my position, minister of a major city church with all its blessings, dignities and responsibilities . . . I'd rather lose my life outright than forfeit these things. I'm weak, I'm weak, my God I'm weak! This is my White Furnace. I need not be weak with God's word within me but since that attack in the press I no longer hear. I've no longer been able to help my people. There are tragedies coming up that need not: a mother dying in hospital, two homes breaking up, a man going mad and a girl lusting . . . I see these things, I know these things! . . . but I go down before the City."

"Mr. Guymer . . . I . . ." I hide my face behind my hands.

"I see Babylon lurching by with no knowledge of, and no wish for the knowledge of . . . the Wisdom, the Master-Sentiment. I see out in the world nuclear weapons in the hands of brilliant statesmen whose morality never developed beyond childhood. Yet a few weeks in the paper have silenced His voice. The Master no longer speaks."

But the first few glasses manage to speak. I lift my face since it's mine. "And what if He doesn't speak? Are we any the worse for that? Forget it all Mr. Guymer. Forget it like the City. Live love and make merry as the rest of us always do. Enter a float from the church for the Blossom Parade and

284

put on it a prophet crucified upside down; then all roar with laughter. Life is short and is going to be shorter."

"And what would I do should I hear His voice?"

"You'll never hear His voice."

"And what would I do should I see His face?"

"You'll never see that either."

"Is this what the City says to me?"

"Yes. Forget it all like us; ignore it all like me. Sin achieves more than sanctity."

"And this sermon I have worked on?"

"Admirable exercise for an overcharged mind. A vent for withheld emotion. Try a medium less exacting, sir. A little pleasurable deviation among women. Burn the sermon Mr. Guymer. You've skipped a step. Saints must be sinners first."

You pull up a chair near me and lift a prosaic foot upon it in your own characteristic way. You place an elbow on the knee and your chin in the hand and study me with concentration. Then your other hand reaches and cups my chin and you examine every feature; your eyes gathering them all up like a shepherd checking his sheep. "Why," you ask quietly at length, "did you ever come to church in the first place?"

"You've got to have somewhere to wear your clothes."

"And when you found other and . . . more profitable places to wear your clothes, more . . . rewarding places . . . why did you continue to come?"

"I'm cursed with a sensitive hearing and your voice has beauty."

"Why have you stopped coming now? Has the quality of my voice declined?"

I pause . . . and rescue my face from your hand. My cocktails do the thinking while I light a cigarette. At length they answer wistfully, "God and I don't get on. We're rivals."

You smile reluctantly at first then turn from me and laugh. Then you take down your foot and lift your head and let a fearful lot go. You walk round the study with it, stop at the window with it and rub your face until suddenly it abates and all your tensions and postures with it. "I'm afraid I have a meeting at eight-thirty," you say briskly. "I want you to wait here for me. In here or in your car." You look down upon me again. "There's still much unsaid. I'll only be an hour . . . then we'll unravel all this. The unsaid accumulates, given time."

Drink accumulates too, given time. You just want to give it time. Then suddenly it hits, and hits hard. Whirl . . . the mind staggers . . . the senses overturn. The whole world with its idolatries, its religion, its weapons, its blossoms, its earthquakes, its love and pain beats in glorious bacchanal. Dances like Grandma's Lullaby. . . .

"Will you meet me in an hour?"

Wait . . . whirl . . . wheel . . . "I'll meet you at the top of the s-summer."

"The top of the summer?"

"M-mid s-summer."

"Midsummer?"

"You may conduct my nuptials then."

"What do you mean?"

"Y'know. Man an' woman say 'I do.' You . . . know-what-I-mean? Till death do us part s-stuff."

"Are you planning to marry?"

"Let no man put as-sunder. Tha' sorta thing. You never heard of Let no man puttasunda?"

"You can't do that!"

" 'You take thish woman to be your wedded-wife?' 'I do.' 'You take thish man to . . .' "

"You can't marry! I want to . . . to talk to you!"

"Thash wha' they all shay."

The door swings open and Hugh appears. "Look here Boss you had that spanner last. Where the devil did you . . . Hail! My glamorous Gomer!"

"I want you to do something for me lad."

"Whoopee! Whacko! Look at our . . . !"

"Listen lad. I want you to . . ."

"Ship ahoy! Whoop-la! Vive la France!"

"Hugh. I want you to go down to the . . ."

"I say are you real? Is that blouse meant to . . . ?"

"Will you go down to the hall and take my teen-agers? Gymnasium? See that they . . ."

"Whew . . . ! What price Paris!"

"Work them hard. Tire them out. Mop up all their surplus energy. Mop up your own too. Put competition into it. Exhaust them. Give them a talk on not abusing policemen on street corners in the exercise of their duty. Give them their Elvis Presley records, give them half an hour of rocking 'n rolling then send them to bed. And I mean bed. Take my car if yours won't go. Good night for the time being I'm . . . busy."

"From angels to delinquents! Give us your key then Boss. Toodle-doo kids. Bye bye fellas."

Closed door, departing steps and down comes the garment of serenity once more; enclosing, enwrapping, encompassing. Returning to your chair at your desk you are the tranquil priest once more. Whole lifetimes go reeling by; yours, mine, Hugh's, the teen-agers', Elizabeth's, her parents', Gordon's, his wife's, Corinne's, the twins', the congregation's, Doctor and Mrs. John's, Stan's, Monsieur's, Dezso's, the minor supports', the Magistrate's, Amos', the City's, New Zealand's, and the Earth's gyrate amid tossing blossom to brilliant inner music . . . all waltzing to Grandma's Lullaby. . . .

I think I hear you speaking and try to brush my eyes. . . . "What were you saying . . . so sorry . . ."

"I was saying you should be down at the hall with my other . . . my OTHER! . . . juvenile delinquents."

"What a big world isn't it . . . whatta lotta people! There you are waltzing to the Lullaby and there's . . . look! . . . there're the orchards waltzing. I . . ."

"I'd think nothing of picking you up and locking you away in the parsonage; clothes, grand piano, grand bed and all."

"Corinne loves me . . . there she is! Dancing! I'm her mother. Corinne is me. She's a little girl with no mother as I was. I'll go back and be my own mother. Then I'll be a good girl. I know what little girls with no mother want. I'll be her mother . . . look! Look at us dancing in the orchard! . . . what are you saying . . ."

"As minister of your church I will need to know more details before permitting your marriage."

"Are sinners so precious to you sir?"

"It's marriage that's so precious. Have you any rules of morality at all?"

"Morality . . . where have I heard that word before?"

"I don't think you've heard it before." Silence. "What happened in your childhood Mrs. Jones?"

"Germaine. That's my name. Germaine de Beauvais. Rue de la Colombe. I'm tired of being Mrs. Jones.

"Yes?"

"That's what I came for . . . to tell you all that. And a lot, a lot more. But I'm not in the mood any longer. And I've changed my mind about what I meant to do . . . and be. I'm too much of a sinner to change. Now. A good pianist doesn't change her style. Now I've got to go. My cocktails might run out. Y'know one of my rules of morality? Never leave a party sober. My husband always carried me home over his shoulder."

"Germaine de Beauvais."

"Don't you tell the press! I don't like reporters. Don't you tell your Ladies' Guild!"

"Germaine . . . do you love this man you plan to marry?"

"Never answer boring questions; another rule of morality."

288

You rise and pocket your hands and move about the study. "The extreme necessity of love," pace . . . pace . . . "and the bitter price of it." Then you return to your desk and sit behind it and lay your two hands separately upon it as though they did not know each other . . . apart . . . while the room, so small an area in the stupendous brilliant world wheels and whirls and reels; a chaos of fissioned hearts and nuclear passions and poised warheads and marriage bells and orchard bouquets and missiles and churches and music masters and Master-Sentiments and magistrates and blossoms and earthquakes lurching and bumping and spinning so that when I think I hear you speaking conversationally to someone else in the room and I brush my eyes and look about I'm not surprised to see no one else in the room.

"Master, speak to me."

Confusion . . . I'm sick . . . catch me. . . .

"Master, speak." Your hands meet each other and mate upon the desk as we two should but your voice is conversational. "Lift this dark blind between me and Your face. Shatter this enclosing wall so that I may hear your voice. I cry to Thee, O Lord, and I call upon Thee. Thou art my God; give ear to my supplication. O my Beloved deliver me from this pit of darkness for I am brought low.

"Master, speak. Let me echo Thy voice. Seek me, that I may seek this erring child, lost and alone. Lead me, that I may lead her wandering wavering feet. Feed me, that I may feed your hungering one.

"Master, speak. Strengthen me that I, firm on a rock and strong in Thee, may stretch out a loving hand to this child wrestling in the troubled sea.

"Teach me, that I may teach her in turn Thy many timeless truths. Wing my words, that they might reach the concealed depths in this young idolatrous heart.

"Master, speak. Give me rest. That I may speak with

soothing power a word to this weary one in her needful hour. Fill me with Thy fullness so that I might overflow with Thy love for her.

"Master, speak. Thy servant heareth. What hast thou to say to me?"

The soft distant bells as you turn to me, your voice simple. "You will return to church tomorrow Germaine. Next week I will call on the various men who aa . . . bring you up and who aa . . . school you in their morality. And as minister of your church I shall relieve you of them. You will give me their names on Monday afternoon. Then I shall include you in my rounds again . . . as usual."

"God curse you!"

"Don't say that!" The chair overturns.

I run across the room to the door. You are there before me. "Take that back."

"I won't."

"You will."

"I won't."

"You will."

"I will *not*. God curse you again."

Soft . . . "Obey me."

"Obey *you*? . . . You . . . you fool of God. You . . . you ineffective . . . impotent . . . half-inch man."

You are trembling and sweating and your fists clench and I back away and you follow. "Don't touch me, don't you . . . touch me." You still follow me and I back against a chair and stagger and fall to the floor on my back and I hold up my hands against you and you stand enormous above me your low hair falling forward and your face wet and your clenched hands trembling.

"You remain till you retract those words."

"I won't."

"You will."

"I won't."

"You will."

"I will not."

"Then . . . GO! And you leave this house without God's blessing! The church can survive without you!" You turn from me and pick up the overturned chair, not me you pick up, and set it on its four legs again in its place as though it meant so much to you and you take out your handkerchief and dry your face, cleaning up with disastrous finality. Cleaning up the mess of me in your life. Both you and God rejecting me. I grasp the chair near me and pull up to my feet and get as far as you and beat at your face. I beat at it and beat at it over and over again. I take a book and beat it with that and spit on your face while you stand and stare in my eyes then I turn from you and reach the door and whisper from there "God curse you. God curse you for all the pain you've brought me. God curse you for all the sin you've brought me. God curse you forever . . . and ever. . . ."

Now I am out on the porch and the night air smacks. The steep steps, I stagger and as I fall your hand grasps my arm and I don't. I hear your breathing and smell the man odour of you. On the bottom step you release me and I try to run in starts and jagged stops across the dewed grass through the street trees and the watching street lights and the sound of bells and I reach my car first easily while you stroll out through the sober shrubs as though you had no other thought than to pick up the evening paper. And I find my seat and slump with my head low until I feel fingers cupping my chin and raising it and moving and tightening in the way I dreamed of and your other hand reaches in and turns my face your way and here is your mouth on mine so briefly that I barely know of your blood on my face and of the destruction of the new life I planned before the kiss is over. "Anyway," you say to me, "bless you."

"Prends pitié de ma longue misère."

I'M THE DRUNK at the door now and the Villain is within.
Now I know what drunks feel like outside church doors and
what brings it about in the first place. And I know what they
dress like too. This one is equipped with a tobacco-brown
pullover belted over slacks in stripes of brown by Abelard and
boots in gold-green calf, does it matter who by. . . . I even
sink on the steps as he used to do I've had to drink so much to
get here. Only you remain unchanged, clothes, preaching,
voice and all. So unforseeable can consequences be.

I don't hear your sermon on Amos of course. For one thing
I can't be expected to work out when it is and for another I'm
quite beyond hearing it anyway . . . unless the voice that
comes through to me as I listen at the door is the sermon.

The wings unfurl and the bird begins rising. "God as
Beauty conserves values in art. God as Truth assures them to

science and philosophy. God as Love nurtures all that is dearest between people. But God as Wisdom!" . . . furl the wings and grounds the bird . . . "unites all these."

A pause . . . I press the door a little ajar. . . .

" 'But where shall wisdom be found?
And where is the place of understanding?
The depth said, it is not with me.
And the sea saith, it is not with me.
It cannot be gotten for gold,
Neither shall silver be weighed for the price thereof.' "

But that could not have been the sermon . . . you said you wanted to talk about Amos. Now I've got to get to my car somehow. Put this foot first . . . hold on. Now the next foot . . . now watch me down these steps . . . take my arm, O Baal. . . .

But you are not beneath the trees when I come out after music late on Monday afternoon, at least not yet, to get the names of my playmates, so while I am waiting for you, an unprecedented thing, I wander out to the gate to pick up the paper. There's nothing unusual of course in reading of a drunken driver in a head-on collision on a straight road in broad daylight . . . except that the driver turns out to be Hugh ClanWilliam and the two killed Mr. and Mrs. Dalgliesh, Eliza's parents. H'm . . . to quote you. Must have been all that Pernod I coaxed Hugh to drink this morning when I lied so cheerfully and said I had managed the week of continence and had turned over my brand-new leaf. Which of course I have not since that moment of your mouth on mine. Who could turn over anything with a memory like that on the mouth . . . and the promise that it left . . . and the message that it gave and the hysteria of my nervous organs. My body has always indicated my direction and has no respect for new leaves. Anyway, where was I . . . don't let me wander . . . oh yes this execution this morning. Where is it again in the paper? Oh down here on this column. Fortunate in a way; all depends how you see it. Now Hugh has achieved that something he was always saying he wanted, to keep his Purity inaccessible so that he might know the inspiration of l'amour. She'll never forgive him for that. He'll have an endless supply of inspiration for the rest of his life and may even learn la grande passion. And even if her Almighty Nameless Nothing requires of her that she should forgive him, an almighty minister won't. Moreover when he is out of hospital he will certainly go to gaol where he will be thoroughly at home among his own delinquents and which he will enjoy to the full as only Hugh could. All of which would add up in the end to a by no means uninteresting minister supposing they released him in time. God works in a mysterious way but Baal is admirably clear.

I walk back beneath the trees you have named Faith, Hope and Charity to the studio to check up once more on my face. You still might come. Ballistic lipstick is kiss-proof and well it may need to be now that our kissing has almost started. The powder is mixed with crushed silk giving a sheen and a glow like petals, my Strontium Ninety with its famous and deadly fall-out I have proved to be passion-proof and the supersonic line of my dress. Receive my incense, O Baal.

My hyacinth on the table has wilted in the thirst of this hollow-eyed, hollow-bodied weekend, which won't do . . . not with the immanence of l'amour. Tip it outside and refill the vase with fresh water. Which flowers shall I have for you? I find myself making my way through the small gate into the orchard with Gordon's clippers and gather long slender branchlets clustered with living white like the white of my slender spring dress. The petals don't fall as I gather them, not one, strongly adhered to their tree; full of confidence they are of consummation to come; today, or tomorrow or tomorrow. They light up my studio when I take them in. They need a bigger bowl. Their slender arms reach out all ways catching all the light and keeping it. I see nothing else with them here; living, shining account of the inner chanson "Waiting."

I listen for your steps then go to the mirror again. On the dressing table is the paper . . . oh yes that. You must have let me wander . . . h'm. So the Prince has gone from Eliza's fairy story and the Ogre has come on stage. An Ogre familiar in Babylon, one with whom you are constantly duelling. The Almighty Idol Drink. Now you will lock up Elizabeth which will make excellent theatre; lock her up in your parsonage as you said you would if the Ogre ever brushed her. Lock her up tightly as you locked up Hugh and as you threatened to lock me up on Saturday . . . in which the city will doubtless delight. You can never charge us as a city with not providing audience. Whatever you do or don't do, say or don't say, whether in blank verse or prose, whomever you lock up or don't, snatch back from death or don't . . . whatever you preach you think of us, whoring or faithful, you can never charge us with not making a rattling good audience. Now where was I again . . . what irresponsible wandering . . . ooh yes, all this makes a damned good story full of the sensation on which Babylon thrives. Maybe Baal has taught you at last that the God you serve is not love.

It is time I heard your steps . . . after the time. I don't see how you could have waited till tomorrow. That was not the message of your mouth. I can read what men's mouths say. I lay the paper down on the bed and try to think which is difficult with the inner music. Thoughts are lost in the chanson like petals before a tornado. Why haven't you come? This thought is clear enough. It rises to the surface of storming ocean over and over again like a man who will not drown. Why haven't you come? Don't tell me, for God's sake . . . I mean Baal's sake . . . that there's going to be more waiting. What will my organs say? Have you traced the cause of the fatality this morning to its source; Germaine de Beauvais? How much do you know? How much do you care? How much are you able to forgive? As much as the Lord I wonder?

Suddenly a cleavage in the music; it divides catastrophically asunder. Rearing up from the surging seas of sound . . . an arm with a pointing finger. I hear a "cry in the morning and an alarm at noon" so that my hands press the middle of my midriff where the swords of l'angoisse begin slicing. . . .

> "Ange plein de gaieté, connaissez-vous l'angoisse,
> La honte, les remords, les sanglots, les ennuis
> Et les vagues terreurs de ces affreuses nuits
> Qui compriment le coeur comme un papier qu'on froisse?
> Ange plein de gaieté, connaissez-vous l'angoisse?"

Your name is not down to preach in the Church Notices column for the following two Sundays, I don't know why. Your place is taken by one of your precious old saints, an octagenarian minister. As the petals of the fruit blossom on the table first wilt, then drop one by one, then in half dozens then in abandoned mass, I take to practising the chansons. Not another exercise for me. I take over these chansons or rather they take over me; "The Bridges of Paris,"

"Waiting," "White Furnace," "Élixir," "The Fire of Your Mouth," "La Majesté des Souffrances Humaines" and "May the Night Bear My Breath Away." I seem to be able to play them for some reason. Through them Léon's whole soul flies from his tongue and at last I understand what it says. Yet he does not come to me either. Have you as you said "relieved me of him"? And of the rest of them too for that matter? You super-Saint George! Yet . . . as I contemplate the fallen white petals all over the table and the floor . . . I doubt if I'm any the worse for it.

Every late afternoon after music I dress in the white super-sonic, tightening daily over my breasts, and go out under the trees. I don't go to Mrs. Doctor John to tell her that her husband never loved me, I don't persuade their only son to sell his deadly motorbike and give up drinking, I don't write to Gordon and renounce him and tell him to return to his wife and give her back her will to live, I don't go to Elizabeth at the parsonage to exonerate Hugh in her eyes, I don't . . . in spite of the vomiting every morning that makes me think of radial arteries and nail files or anything else that's sharp enough, the end of a scissors or something . . . go to Léon to acknowledge his child within me that cannot be consigned like a lover's letter to consuming flame . . . and marry, I don't go to the hospital to Hugh and I don't go to you yourself in repentance. Baal holds me with glittering golden hands adjuring me from clouds of incense to

"Let him that glorieth glory in this
that he understandeth and knoweth me, for
I AM BAAL!
Which exercise hate, injustice and selfishness in the
Earth:
For in these things I delight!"

There are still some determined petals clinging to the fruit branches in the bowl on the third Saturday when I drive into your city in the afternoon. To watch the Blossom Parade; you'll certainly not be on your rounds on a public day like this with your a-whoring City dressed like the princess of Jerusalem before her fall. And I stand amid the thrilled clapping crowds in the narrow main thoroughfare among the flags and bunting and the blossoms and the triumphant music of many bands and the visitors overflowing from the trains. I stand on my toes trying to see over festive shoulders, looking for the floats from Gordon's firms and especially the one from his orchard carrying Elizabeth the Spirit of Spring. All of which the Villain had been organising, none of which appear let alone win first prize. And for the church float too which does not appear either, with or without a Prophet crucified, upside down or rightside up. So that I lose interest and find myself pushing and writhing through the delighted cheering crowds propelled by some surging implacable thirst no longer of the senses but of something deep in the uncharted area of sentiment . . . towards I know not what; past the tall Clock Tower rearing into the blue, across the railway line severing the city waistline, down blocks of verandahed shops as far as the house called by God's name and edge in through its deserted side door and entering the temple-of-the-Lord, the-temple-of-the-Lord braving its quiet high holiness and across the carpeted nave and up the steps into your pulpit and I look upon the open pages of your great Bible ever so much a part of you and read just what I chance to see here which turns out to be a conversation between some man and some woman at a well:

"Jesus answered and saith unto her, whosoever drinketh of this water shall thirst again:

But whosoever drinketh of the water that I shall give him shall never thirst; . . .

The woman saith unto him, Sir, give me of this water, that I thirst not."

But the next morning when the third Sunday uncovers its unpowdered face and the last of the blossom petals have fallen all over the table and floor and the fruit-arms reach bleakly pleading, by the time this third Sunday wakes upon its desperate godless day I can at last see that ministers like magistrates don't forgive like the Lord . . . nor even the Lord himself for that matter. It is plain to me now that God hates me. That's all I've learnt about God so far; that he has industriously dug for me this Pit and he knew just how to go about it, exactly where to put his finger . . . upon my too-sensitive-passionate organs. He hates me with a personal jealousy far worse than anyone's wife does. He hates me because you love me. He is indeed my Almighty Rival against whose power I am nothing. It's true he is a jealous God. But some power is left in my hands, just enough to save myself. I can at least change l'angoisse. I can't escape it apparently but I can certainly change its geography. I can at least change its address. Since it's got to be. And even were all this not so . . . were he not the Almighty Villain in my life . . . his voice is too loud for people like me.

In the late afternoon when intellects and emotions are at their best and birdsong most exhilarating, instead of preparing for your church, even though your name is at last down again to preach, I prepare for something less arduous.

I pull out my overseas trunk from behind the relic and brush the dust from upon it, then stand and try to work out what to put in first. As a matter of fact you put shoes in first and then on top of them you put things that don't crush like lingerie. You can roll nylon into balls and it still unfolds all right. Then you start on clothes proper. At the end of the wardrobe where I begin here is the de-lustred satin the white concert gown I was wearing at Raoul's last concert taking the solo of the concerto with the orchestra when he pitched over dead from the rostrum with his baton still in his hand. For some reason I absolutely have to put this on and I slip off the housecoat and nightdress I'm still in and pull on this fairy-tale affair with its skirt of multiple trills and cadenzas and undo my hair and let it cascade like the terrible princess of Jerusalem before her fall and put on the record of the concerto and glide to the long mirror and stand before it saying adieu to you; to you who view perfectly normal things like drinking and love-making and speeding as monstrous and forbidden and who have introduced me to the idea of iniquity so that I am facing the door in my satin and hair when it opens in a way I know and you appear in a way I know you come in dressed for church you the Reverend Guymer.

Why you stand still looking at me like this for so long I don't know but in time you come to me and take my hand and put it back in your pocket with your own and lay your cheek to mine and now your mouth on mine and you breathe in my throat "Release . . ." so that there is no longer the length of the church between us nor the infinite weight of it upon us and so that as the kissing at last starts and as the flames in the grate utter a gasp for breath and as the Three Trees outside jerk in sudden stress and as the concerto works surely and powerfully through its mounting rhythms . . . you give me back my vineyards.

"I will betroth thee unto me for ever; yea I will betroth thee unto me in righteousness and in justice and in lovingkindness and in mercy. I will even betroth thee unto me in faithfulness and thou shalt know the Lord. . . .

"Thou shalt abide as mine many days; thou shalt not play the harlot and thou shalt not be for another man. So will I also be to thee."

300

Mon esprit, tu te meus avec agilité . . .

MON DIEU . . . what a mess Babylon is in! Tornadoes have no respect for blossoms. As I drive through the main street later to church the City is the terrible princess of Jerusalem *after* her fall. Everywhere the great composite bouquet is patterned like wreaths on a grave. Flowers, flowers on many a grave; on the graves of righteousness, justice, lovingkindness and mercy. The ravished shop fronts, the ravaged decorated lampposts, the raped streamers of flags, coloured light bulbs and drapes, the blossoms of the Welcome to Babylon signs swinging aloft from one side of the street to the other . . . all torn like the clothes from a whore. All those weeks of intensive joyful work are a wreath on one vast grave, and the tall tragic Clock Tower surveying it all, weeping like Rachel for her children.

There are not many cars, very few, at the house called by

God's name so I'm able to park quite close. Yet even so, walking back to the church through the rising savagery of the storm the black-and-white lightning suit with the heavenly buttons and with hell-prongs painted on the gloves is ruined. Rain thrashes me like the final judgment with thrashing instruments of iron so that this electrifying creation from the hand of man expires at the hand of God. Along with the concert gown now its fate is the jumble-stall; together with the Russian jacket ruined in the orchards the indigo that Léon tore up and the demoted Chinese gown. The capacity of a man of God to decimate a wardrobe is a matter for future reflection. Also I'm late of course but for an astonishingly different reason. So is the preacher himself late for that matter but there's hardly anyone here to record it.

Not quite so fearfully as before I step, the transgressor, into the high hymning holiness, the singing and righteousness and the fragrance of forgiveness. No longer is the nave packed right up to the sacramental table, no chairs in the aisles, no people standing in the choir area and at the side and back doors; visitors from afar for the Blossom Parade. Just that handful of grey hair at the back, your precious old saints, as it was when I first came. They are standing singing when I edge my wet way in to the chair just within the door and you are sitting out of sight. There is none of that feeling in the church of suppressed expectancy before the curtain goes up in a theatre, or when you leave backstage to walk upon a concert platform. Less fearfully than usual, vastly less afraid, I lift my eyes to the pulpit.

But when the human voices are at last silent and the storm voices take over, when the grey hair sits down and you in your turn rise and see me you are unable for the moment to begin. Where is your practised discretion that you should forget your sermon? Where is your famous trained overlay of serenity that has ever graced this pulpit; your tranquillity borrowed from God? Your face turned upon me is still the face of an hour ago with kisses warming the air. Crisis that is utmost.

I smile. All the way over the heads of the congregation at the back with their middle-class millinery and their uncut hair, over the empty pews in the middle where the stylish and young used to be, and over the vacant seats at the front where the newly come agog liked to sit, all the way from the back of the church to the front . . . I smile. All the way over the tameless passions and tears and agonies and raptures of the ending spring . . . I smile. And all the way over the hollow pews and the pathetic group of saints, from the front of the church to the back, all the way over your renunciations and laborious years . . . you smile back at me. It takes the smile of a sinner barely within the door of a church for a man of God to recover. Down comes the raiment of serenity. Once more the worn cloak descends, familiar now and thinning. Once more we have with us our controlled preacher, our orderly and ordinary priest, and the man of men I have so recently encountered in all his radiant humanity is again the man of God.

I am not aware when you actually begin your sermon because sitting here at the back of the church with the thunder of the elements without and the thunder of the music within, like the thunder of the Master speaking . . . it is beyond a human being to hear. Moreover with your words of love in mind I am hardly the ideal listener. But when I do look up and try I find you have begun steadily enough, softly even with the care of one holding a bird. But no one can hear what you're saying with the competition of the storm outside and after a while you leave the pulpit and walk down the steps and into the nave and from there across the front and then down the aisle until you are standing back here among us. Someone moves along a pew to be nearer, the deaf gentleman I think, then another moves nearer until a general movement brings us all clustered round you like children at

305

story time so that finally as you lift your notes we do at last hear and against the cracking tempest we find you again on the subject of Amos . . . with no bird breaking loose to beat the topmost pillars . . . speaking very softly.

". . . a herdsman on the mountains of Judah and a gatherer of sycamore fruit. Living alone among the lofty crags, the bottomless ravines, the overhanging cliffs and the rushing torrents and the caves; among the bears, wolves, lions and leopards in a country so sparse that 'no two walked together unless they be agreed.' Yet at the call of God he steps from the mountainous harshness into the wealth and idolatry of the two kingdoms, takes up his position in the market place of the border town of Bethel and the Word he interpreted there we read thirty centuries later.

"But what was the response of the people?" We lean forward to catch it. " 'O thou seer, flee thee away into Judah, and there eat bread, and prophesy there: but prophesy not again at Bethel for it is the King's chapel and the King's court.' And what was his answer, my people?" If only you would lift your voice just a little . . . we edge nearer still. "Did he defy them, continue to prophesy, continue to guide and chide them, to meet at last the fate of other golden prophets: thrown alive in a pit, sawn in half or crucified upside down? He did, my people, go home. He DID flee him away into Judah and there dictated alone to a scribe, dressing his gifts in bitterness."

You pause a moment, lift a page, turn it over and study the next. Then you drop your voice if anything rather than challenge the elements outside. Without any of your personal passion left to cloud the meaning I can follow every word. "God gives bitterness to us all, my people, but he also gives us gifts. Is it for us to dress these gifts in our own personal bitterness with agonies our change of garment? Am I to squander what gifts he gave me in courting one stubborn city? God may use all he gave me to court his a-whoring

306

world with love my changes of garment. He may pick me up where he put Amos down, thirty centuries later. I'll spend no more of his precious time on the routine chores of a circuit; a market place runs itself. I'll preach God's word till I'm courting Baal himself. I'll court him in his own language, I'll court him in his own haunts and I'll court him in his own vile ways. Into every one of his accursed idols I will infuse the Spirit so that when we burn lambs at his feet, charge the air with incense about his head and sacrifice to him the flesh of our very souls it will be to God himself. Through me, ignorant, passionate, mortal man may God speak his despisèd word. So that through you, ignorant, passionate, mortal people, in the streets, in the market place, in the theatre and concert hall, in the gaols, the hospitals and asylums, on the road, in the pubs, and in homes and in shops, in every place from the Magistrate's Court to the wonderful Festival of the Blossoms, may he speak his despisèd word.

"Men will cease to pollute heaven and earth when God commands them not to. Never will I flee me away into Judah there to dictate alone to a scribe. Neither will I be buried in a pit, sawn in half or crucified upside down. Never will I hearken unto our death-men to 'Flee away . . . prophesy not. . . .'

 " 'I belong to the great church which holds
 the world within its starlit aisles:
 that claims the great and good of every race and clime:
 that finds with joy the grain of good in every creed,
 and floods with light and love the germs of good in every
  soul.' "

Some tree under stress is violently uprooted and tossed against the window near the pulpit, breaking it, announcing the tornado upon us. Glass scatters everywhere, the gale turns furiously the pages of the Bible in the fervour of its elemental sympathy and your notes lift and fly. But what is a trifling tornado matched with a line of thought? How trivial the tumult of elements beside the intention of man. Even I, a sinner, can see it.

You stand quietly before us, your hair lifting from this side to that and your gown swinging willfully. Smoothing your notes you relax in an easier stance, as though the thunder of the heavens and the passions of the earth were little more than noises off; if anything your voice is lower; it has a flowing quality almost:

" 'Thus saith the Lord:
 "For three transgressions of this Earth, and for four,
 I will not turn away the punishment thereof;
 because you thrash the helpless with thrashing instruments of iron:
 because you deliver whole nations into captivity
 and not remember the brotherly covenant;
 because you pursue your brother with a sword,
 and you cast off all pity,
 and your anger tears perpetually,
 and you keep your wrath forever.

 "Because you rip up the women with child of your
   neighbour
 that you might enlarge your border;
 because you despise the law of the Lord,
 and do not keep his commandments,
 and your lies cause you to err.
 Because you sell the righteous for silver
 and the poor for a pair of shoes;
 you trample the head of the poor into the dust of the
   earth,
 you turn aside the way of the meek,
 and a man and his father will go in unto the same maid
 to profane my holy name.

 "Is it not even thus, O ye children of the Earth?
 Doth not Wisdom cry?

But ye commanded the prophets, saying . . . Prophesy
   not!

"Therefore . . .
I will cause the sun to go down at noon
and I will darken the earth in a clear day;
and I will turn your feasts into mourning,
and all your songs into lamentation:
and I will bring up sackcloth upon all loins
and baldness upon every head;
and I will make it as the mourning for an only son,
and the end hereof as a bitter day.

"Ye have built houses of hewn stone
but ye shall not dwell in them;
ye have planted pleasant vineyards
but ye shall not drink wine of them;
for I will send a radio-active fire unto The Earth
which shall devour the civilisation hereof."
" 'Thus saith the Lord.' "

You fold your pages absently
" 'Prepare to meet thy God, O Earth.' "

I don't rise with the others when the benediction is over to
move towards the door; I'm far from feeling myself. In this
vacuum of the discharged spirit I don't seem to be me at all; a
feeling I've had increasingly over the passionate spring behind. Am I anyone at all? Perhaps I am everyone; the sym-
bol of a city. Indeed and indeed, sitting here in this house
called by God's name saying This is the temple of the
Lord, the temple of the Lord, the temple of the Lord . . .
with a city divorce immanent, an only son estranged, an
eminent musician silent, two parents speed victims, yes a
mother with a child dying, her life ripped up that I might
enlarge my border, a young man in the hospital, his ministry

in limbo, and waiting to go to prison . . . isn't that all now? . . . no floats from Gordon's orchards and . . . I'll have to add this I suppose . . . a minister rejecting his pulpit . . . a good score, what? Sitting here alone at the back of a church, a transgressor, wet through, in a jagged black-and-white lightning suit with its buttons from heaven and its gloves from hell, with prongs painted on my hands and whoredom painted on my heart . . . what loud music within! All about "des souffrances humaines," far too thunderous! . . . or is it the storm, or the voice of God . . . where was I again . . . oh yes, sitting here alone I could well be the whole depraved world. With the weight of the church upon me I am the earth with God's eyes upon me.

I begin to feel her bated breath and her terrorstruck apprehension. I am both sinner and sinned against. I am all the mothers mourning only sons; all the women with child ripped up to enlarge a border. I am the helpless thrashed with thrashing instruments of iron; I'm a maid serving both man and his father. I am the poor with head beaten into the dust of the earth; the righteous sold for silver and the sad for a pair of shoes. I am my brother pursued with a sword and a nation swept to captivity. I am the meek turned aside from my way. I have not remembered the brotherly covenant and I've cast off all pity. My anger against God tears perpetually and I keep my wrath forever. My lies have caused me to err, I have despised the law of the Lord, I have not kept his commandments and little more than an hour ago I have profaned his holy name.

I rise at last in my absolutely-have-to manner I don't know why and begin moving one way or another I don't know which it's not towards the door though . . . ooh am I going to vomit . . . I am walking up the aisle where am I going? . . . how dreadfully loud is the music, too thunderous and cacophanous for people like me. What's this crunching under my feet, ooh yes that glass from the window . . . oooh! look what I've done on the carpet. This-is-the-temple-of-the-Lord-the-temple-of-the-Lord-the-temple-of-the-Lord! . . . oh? here's the pulpit above me. Up the carpeted steps, more crunching glass . . . oooh! look at your steps now. What am I doing up here . . . the-temple-of-the-Lord-the-temple-of-the . . . oh here's your great Bible this book that has so both alarmed and enthralled me this spring . . . the-temple-of-the-Lord-the-temple-of . . . and your notes heaped beside it, your last page on top with its last sentence "Prepare to meet thy God O Earth." But *I* am the Earth am I not? Yes I'm the whole wicked Earth . . . the-temple-of-the . . . and it's time the Earth repented you said. The thunder is too loud, the music is too wild and my sins beyond mending, the thunder is too loud, it is God's voice, it is the Master speaking . . . it's time I the Earth repented . . .

Prepare to meet my God. Well I'd better read this book. You often hear of people opening the Bible at random and finding the very thing. Here's a verse that might do, Job forty-two five: "I have heard of thee by the hearing of the ear, but now mine eye seeth thee. Wherefore I abhor myself . . ." what's this next line? The first tears I can remember blot it out, falling heavily in my soul. "Dust and ashes"? no "blood and ashes" isn't it. . . .

Here's a large piece of glass right here near the book it can't be here for nothing. I take off both the gloves with the hell-prongs painted on them and wrap one over the wide edge of the glass just the very thing, leaving the corner end free. The music's too loud for people like me. I can't stand it, I can't stand it . . . where's this artery you all talk about, some time ago you showed me, this one? Come on Germaine get it over. But I can't see for tears . . . oo-ooh! all over your Bible . . . the music . . . White Furnace . . . come on Germaine get it over. My whole life I've burnt incense to idols when I could have burnt incense to love.

Blossoms blossoms blossoms in clouds . . . skies full of blossoms, blossoms pink blossoms white, myriad petals a-massing, the whole vaulted blue spring sky clustering with clouds of blossom, revolving, spiralling, gyrating in slow majestic dignity and the sound of voices singing aloud . . .

The music is softer now . . . much better, much better. Some hymn, a congregation. The music is softening, dying . . . dying . . . The Lord is my shepherd, I shall not want;
he maketh me to lie;
in pastures green; he leadeth me
the quiet waters by.

The quiet waters by . . .
quiet waters . . .
quiet.